The Meat Goats of Caston Creek
The essential companion for
raising meat goats and country living

SYLVIA TOMLINSON

REDBUD PUBLISHING COMPANY
Victoria, TX

REDBUD PUBLISHING COMPANY
P.O. Box 4424
Victoria, TX 77903

Scott Peck, M. D., *Denial of the Soul,* Published by Harmony Books, a division of Crown Publishers, Inc. Reprinted by permission of The Crown Publishing Group – From *"The Re-Enchantment of Everyday Life"* by Thomas Moore © 1966 by Thomas Moore, Published by HarperCollins Publishers Inc. – *From Fields Without Dreams* by Victor Davis Hanson © 1966, Published by Free Press Paperbacks – From "Allan's Observations", January 1997 Stockman Grass Farmer, Rideland, MS. Reprinted by Permission – From *The Forage Sampler,* April 1998, by Kent Mills, Hermleigh, TX. Reprinted by Permission. – From Acres USA May 1998, "Generating Soil Fertility on Farm" by Joe Salatin. Reprinted by permission of Acres USA, Metairie LA – From "Ranchers' Rights" by Bob Kingsbery © 1990, Woodinville WA 98082. Used by permission.

THE MEAT GOATS OF CASTON CREEK
© 2007, by Sylvia Tomlinson
Revised First Edition 2007
Cover and interior design © TLC Graphics, *www.TLCGraphics.com*

ISBN: 0-9720293-3-8
ISBN: 978-0-9720293-3-9

Tomlinson, Sylvia 1946 -
1st edition 1999
Revised 1st edition 2007

1. Meat Goat Ranching 2. Sustainable Agriculture 3. Anatolian Shepherd Livestock Guardian Dogs 4. Country Living 5. Recipes

DEDICATION

To my husband and soul mate, Steve,
who opened the door to my agrarian dreams

Foreword

In the mid-1990s when the federal government ended its longtime policy of subsidizing the price of mohair, thousands of ranchers were left with millions of head of Angora goats whose hair was no longer worth the price of shearing. In an effort to keep their operations profitable and maintain their ranching lifestyle, many of these producers imported the beefy Boer goat from South Africa to breed to these Angora goats.

Almost overnight, many of these mohair producers became goat meat producers. The timing of the Boer goat's introduction into the United States, the ending of mohair subsidies, plus the explosive influx of Hispanic, Middle Eastern, African and Caribbean immigrants into our country for economic and political reasons, have all worked together to make meat goat production the fastest growing livestock segment in the U.S. today.

Practically every metropolitan area in the country today has a large ethnic community of Muslim and/or Hispanic residents whose preferred choice of meat is goat. In fact, goat is the preferred meat around the world. America and its Western counterparts are unique in their preference for beef and pork. The confluence of all these factors has made the demand for goat meat surge, and in spite of more people than ever producing meat goats, we are falling far short of supply. There are few occupations in the United States today where we can say that demand exceeds supply. Fortunately, goat ranchers fall into that category.

We have the product, we have the market — our challenge now is to produce enough of that product at a reasonable cost to meet this new demand and at the same time provide a reasonable return on our investments of time and money. Goat producers — or those who aspire to be goat producers — must educate themselves on how to best meet these new challenges. In the pages of this book, Sylvia Tomlinson relates her and her family's own experiences in building their meat goat herd on Caston Creek Ranch in Eastern Oklahoma. Any goat producer will tell you that hands-on experience is the best teacher, but it doesn't hurt to have some idea of what you are getting into!

I first came to know Sylvia in 1996 when I launched Goat Rancher magazine — a melding of my 20 years of newspaper experience, an idea to raise meat goats and the desire to move back to my family farm. I don't even remember how Sylvia found out about Goat Rancher, but after submitting an article for publication in just our second issue in June 1996, I quickly recruited Sylvia to become Goat Rancher's first fulltime columnist. She was just launching her goat operation on Caston Creek Ranch and was anxious to share the practical things she had learned about meat goat production — from electric fencing to working pens to guardian dogs. In addition to the technical aspects of goat raising, Sylvia also explored the philosophical aspects of ranching through her writings about sustainable agriculture in general and about the joys and challenges of farm life in particular. It wasn't long before I dubbed Sylvia Tomlinson the "soul" of Goat Rancher magazine.

Through the years Sylvia added to her list of ranch and life experiences, and in 1999 published "The Meat Goats of Caston Creek" — still one of the few books that addresses the challenges of commercial meat goat production. Now, Sylvia has revised her original book with updated information for the continually growing meat goat industry. In addition to her practical as well as whimsical observations on meat goat production, she has included detailed management advice from Dr. Frank Pinkerton, also known as "The Goat Man".

While preparing to write this introduction, I was thumbing through my tattered copy of the first edition of "Caston Creek" and recalled that a friend had complained to me recently about the problems he was having with his commercial herd — some of the illnesses his goats had experienced, how the operation was not meeting his expectations. I laid down my copy of the book and sent my friend an e-mail. I told him to go back and read his copy of "The Meat Goats of Caston Creek". Within its pages was advice on his particular goat health problem, but — more importantly — inspiration to renew his spirit and look at his goat operation in its entirety and the positive impact it has made on his land, his life and his family. That is the kind of inspiration that no one delivers quite like Sylvia Tomlinson.

— TERRY HANKINS
Editor & Publisher
Goat Rancher Magazine

Acknowledgment

A large thank you goes to Terry Hankins, editor and publisher of *The Goat Rancher Magazine,* who after receiving my first offering years ago, asked me if I could "do it every month". I wrote "Caston Creek Chronicles" under the pen name of "La Femme Chevre".

Without the agrarian experience, there might have been no story for us on Caston Creek. New experiences bring new wisdom and many people contributed to our knowledge bank.

During the days of our journey along the learning curve, icons in the goat community, like Dr. Frank "The Goat Man" Pinkerton, shared advice freely and influenced many of our decisions. We are delighted that Dr. Pinkerton, encouraged by his lovely wife Jean, has graciously agreed to enrich this edition with his offerings. And, as if that weren't treat enough, Dr. Pinkerton's friend and colleague, Dr. Ken McMillan, added his contribution.

Last but not least, warm thanks to Gene Blackwell for the wonderful photos that have become a part of this book. And always, my profound love and gratitude goes to my family for always believing in me.

— Sylvia Tomlinson

Introduction

Our family had been absentee owners of "*the ranch*" for decades while the local population used it for their personal hunting and fishing grounds. Some even cut the timber, albeit illegally, to supplement their incomes. In the fall of 1986, during the dark days of the oil industry, we moved to the ranch. We were newly married, arriving with hopes and expectations, and my four young children in tow. The ranch consisted of an eight hundred eighty acre patch of neglected and alternately abused land. Rocky and overgrown with brush, weeds, scrub oak and pine timber, it is located in the foothills of the Ouachita Mountain Range in Southeastern, Oklahoma.

Naively, we thought we could make a living on the ranch. Initially, we bought thirty-nine head of all the wrong kind of cattle, bottled over eighty dairy calves, and tried confined sow farrowing on the advice of a local expert whose experience turned out to be raising a pet pig or two. Looking back, one could say that all of those attempts at farming and ranching were miserable failures. We like to say that they were merely guide posts along the learning curve pointing us to a better way of doing things. We eventually built a quality herd of registered Salers cattle, and later a herd of registered and commercial meat goats. More importantly, we began a process of renewal as we returned to the land as stewards in training. We learned quickly the need to utilize low-input farming techniques.

Low input farming alone did not give us the capital we needed to make investments in livestock and improvements in fencing and facilities. We discovered we needed off-farm jobs.

We experienced many of the same struggles that belie the America farmer today. Farming profitably requires an edge. For the small farmer this is often diversification. We looked to meat goats for that opportunity and they have served us well. However, any new venture means new things to learn and raising goats was no exception.

We began 1998 with over three hundred head of breeding meat goat does and one hundred head of bred cows and heifers. It seemed that we had finally reached the point where we needed to either go forward with our plans to ranch full-time, cut back dramatically, or give it up. The previous year had been difficult as we juggled a full-time job with long distance ranching by phone.

Allan Nation's January 1997 "Allen's Observations" column in the *Stockman GrassFarmer Magazine* continued to haunt me as I recalled his warning that, "you can't split your mental energy and be successful. Your mind has to be on one thing… There is a 'window of opportunity' open now for people who want to become full-time ranchers, but it will not last but a couple of years."

We began to spend more time at the ranch, relinquishing the certain paycheck for the uncertainties of agriculture. At first, we expected to use the goats as brush busters, creating more grass for the cattle. We did not plan to eliminate the browse entirely but rather manage it as a renewable forage resource for the goats. We knew it would take time and practice to fine-tune these grass farmer skills.

With the meat goat market growing rapidly, we adjusted our long term thinking to consider meat goats rather than cattle as number one. Goats are also an enjoyable and manageable livestock choice for folks like us who are approaching (or well past) retirement age.

So for a time we were known as the goat folks on Caston Creek and you could find us at the ranch tending the goats and looking forward to another kidding season. But life in its unpredictable way threw us a few curves with some health problems and then one of those events that only happen to "other people" – our home burned to the ground, and nearly with us in it. Heartbroken and in shock, we returned to the familiar Texas oil patch, unsure of how we wanted to re-invent our lives.

As this book goes to press, we are once again looking to the banks of Caston Creek where we first lived our agrarian dreams. With a little luck, we'll spend some of our retirement there reminiscing about the good ol' days.

Table of Contents

PART ONE

A Little About Us

*La Femme Chevre
with Tex and Babe*

Papa

Sharing the journey with the next generation.

CHAPTER ONE

Destined to be Goat Ranchers

I t all really started several years ago when we fell in behind a pickup load of Spanish nannies and their new babies on their way to the sale barn. It was love at first sight. The next thing Papa knew he was sitting ringside with Nana who was urging him to bid on every goat and kid that entered the sale. Fortunately, only thirty goats sold that day. Fearful that some poor nanny's maternal bond would be prematurely severed from her adoring offspring, we took every one home.

The goats adopted an old barn for shelter at night. Next they efficiently cleaned all the fencerows around it. Then they taught us a valuable lesson: Goat Ranching Requires Effective Fences. The goats began to wander over to spend the day with a neighboring cow herd. The cows were unflappable but this particular neighbor did not care for the additional livestock. The goats would have undoubtedly improved his pasture by eating much that the cows would not. In eastern Oklahoma that includes cedar, green briar and poison ivy. In order to avoid a feud, we sold the goats and decided that some day we would try again.

Perhaps destiny cannot be changed. In the summer of 1994, we found ourselves working in southwest Texas, a land of mesquite trees, prickly pear, windmills and GOATS! We saw that goats could be a serious and viable business endeavor so we began to read and research. We picked the brain of every goat rancher we could find and hoped that our experience with cattle would provide some positive transfer and shorten the learning curve. Still, we waited.

And then it happened. One spring day in Texas we found some goats. It was only a short time before things started happening back on Caston Creek. Barn remodeling and pen building became the order of the day. Our fence lesson was not forgotten. We experimented with everything including making pens using sturdy woven horse wire. The pens would provide protection until the larger, more remote areas had better fences and guard dogs.

Papa had grown accustomed to calling me "Nana" after the arrival of the grandkids, but with the goat population growing, he dubbed me "La Femme Chevre." I think because it sounds better than "goat woman". Forty head of Spanish and Kiko cross goats and kids found a home on Caston Creek. We jumped the gap between idea and reality. We were in the goat business with plans to grow!

CHAPTER TWO

Goat Fever Strikes

Any new venture holds the promise of unexpected happenings and new things to learn but for the rookie goat rancher, there's more. There is a growing subculture in rural America called Goat Ranchers!

Goat ranchers are not your ordinary folk. They are the salt of the earth. Goat ranchers enjoy the innate charm of the inquisitive goat and find satisfaction in experiencing the stewardship of such intelligent, stubborn, curious and delightful creatures. Goat ranchers seem more focused on practical matters and less concerned with the image they are projecting to their neighbors and friends. Whether transporting goats in a beat up old trailer or in the back seat of a Town Car, a common thread runs through the fabric of the goat rancher's soul.

One can become a goat rancher in a variety of ways. You can be born into it. This is a very sensible way to do it since someone else has learned a lot of the tough lessons for you. You don't have to reinvent the wheel, as Papa says. Another way to get into this business is to catch the goat fever. When this happens, there is no sense fighting it. You might as well give in and let it run its course. The fever will subside eventually and be replaced by a chronic condition called goat ranching. It is characterized by general satisfaction, a sense of accomplishment and pride in producing more dollars per acre with goats than with other livestock.

Papa and I got the fever bad. It helped that we were both equally afflicted. We had the attack shortly after we'd bought our first goats. We decided we needed more.

The old ranch truck had been worked too hard to be trusted on a trip longer than a run to the feed store. Not to be discouraged, we hooked up the rusty old cattle trailer with the faded blue paint job to the oldest daughter's new extended cab truck and headed to Southwest Texas.

We covered over 1,000 miles in all, stopping to pick up two Anatolian pups from the Robert and Jean Ebeling Angora Goat Ranch. Jean met us with a friendly smile and a firm handshake and I knew in an instant that this was a woman to be admired. The reading of her book, "Angora Goats and Guard Dogs" gave us a lot of confidence. With the help of a couple of good dogs, we felt sure that we could raise goats along Caston Creek amidst the eastern Oklahoma coyotes and bobcats.

The pups were almost weaned and had been in the company of some pretty classy Angora Goats. They traveled in the cab with us, sleeping most of the time like babies do, while we tried out different names for them. We knew the two fluff balls would play an important part in our goat ranching future.

We arrived before dark at the rock ranch house of long time goat rancher Stuart Speck. He had promised us the cream of his doe crop and he didn't let us down. A beautifully uniform assortment of multicolored Spanish and Spanish/Boer crossbred nannies were waiting. We finished looking at the goats as the sun went down and Stuart and his fiancée, Carla, threw some steaks on the mesquite and hickory fired grill. The dry south wind carried the smell of burning cedar embers across the yard as we listened to the evening sounds on the prairie and plied the experienced goat rancher with questions. We learned that orphans were called "sanchos" and we talked about the importance of good management and things such as the condition of the doe at breeding.

We were all up early to sift the best does to take home. The fever was running high and when Stuart offered the pick of a few of his best young mama nannies to fill the trailer, we couldn't resist. We were almost ready to go but there was still space in the bed of the truck. We borrowed a wire cage and stuffed it with nineteen bloomy new-borns fresh off their mamas. We pulled out, heading East, with a total of eighty-six female goats. We didn't say much for the first few miles, then looked at each other, laughed and said, "We're in the goat business, are we crazy?" Yeah, ain't it great, we thought.

A call home, to tell the crew to get the milk replacer ready, generated comments about Goats Anonymous. The trip back was blissfully uneventful. A quick stop by the vet clinic to pick up the health papers and we headed home. We heard the vet mutter something about coyote bait. Guess he hadn't noticed our two big tough guard dogs.

The pups slept in the back of the cab with two newborn does. Papa and I finally decided to name the male 'Tex', in honor of the state of his birth, and the female 'Babe'. She's was definitely a bit of a porker and we were pretty sure she was already talking to her does.

*Madeline Grace visits the does
in the weaning pen.*

Grandkids (left to right) Katie, Christian, and Curtis with fall kids.

CHAPTER THREE

The Kids
Come Home

T he children have all grown up and left home. Many are married and have little ones of their own now. Papa and I feel blessed when they return to the ranch each year for the annual event that we like to call our Turkeyfest. Often bringing a friend or two, the family gathers to celebrate Thanksgiving at the ranch.

It's a good time to reminisce since we arrived in this backwoods corner of Oklahoma early in November of 1986. We celebrated our first Thanksgiving with some of the two-legged kids and a neighbor couple. It was the beginning of a new marriage for Papa and I and we had the job ahead of us to blend our families.

Such endeavors require some work. The Brady Bunch is more a Hollywood myth than a magic recipe. Nevertheless, with commitment, perseverance, love and hard work, we have become a family. Sitting around the Thanksgiving table, we can all look back, laughing and groaning at the mistakes we made.

Putting a family together was not the only hard work. We had to learn to ranch while reclaiming an abused, overgrown piece of land. We had read plenty but putting it into action was another matter. We made a lot of mistakes. The kids like to remind me of the time we bottled over eighty dairy calves. They hated washing the bottles, mixing milk replacer, and getting covered with calf slobbers. My teenage daughters began thinking they had been exiled to the land before time where there would never be life after bottle babies.

Life did continue on, bringing its inevitable changes. Most of the bottle babies grew up, as did the kids, and we moved on to other experiments in sustainable agriculture. Some of our attempts to farm profitably crashed and burned. Still, there were bright spots. Our choice of Salers cattle rewarded us with a good doing, low maintenance, grass-harvesting animal that was tolerant to our journey along the learning curve.

We continued trying different management schemes and fencing arrangements. We continued to look for something else to diversify our agricultural base and bring us home to ranch full-time. The off-farm jobs that we were trained for meant traveling to distant county seats. This meant we lost not only the lifestyle we wanted but also the chance for daily input at the ranch.

We looked to goat ranching as a possible solution to making the ranch profitable. Goats might balance the economics of cattle ranching and they would definitely improve the pasture. We chose Kiko and Spanish goats for the same reason we chose Salers cattle. We knew we must have a hardy, vigorous animal in our neck of the woods to harvest the browse and grass.

About the time we decided to get goats, we got three hundred cinnamon queen laying pullets. They grew beautifully and began laying only to be largely eaten by the guard dogs who missed the class on guarding chickens. No doubt on the Anatolian Plains of Turkey, guardian dogs are not brought "Hunter's Choice" dog food daily and must provide their own meals.

We are still contemplating the addition of blueberries, another challenge, and another opportunity. It will go well or it won't. In years to come we hope that we'll be able to laugh at our stumbling along this part of the learning curve.

Every Thanksgiving we are thankful for our health and family, thankful for the freedoms we have as Americans, and thankful that we can still pursue our dream to ranch full-time. Oh yes, and one more thing, we are thankful for enough eggs to make an omelet.

PART TWO

About Does
and Bucks

This young Kiko doe is ready for breeding.

Nine-year-old "Moneymaker" is still an eager beaver.

CHAPTER FOUR

How Old Should Doelings Be For Breeding?

There's an old adage that comes to mind at breeding time: An Ounce Of Prevention Is Worth A Pound Of Cure. Like many of our learning experiences in the goat business, this bit of wisdom is one that came to be embraced after chasing a cure because we either neglected or forgot to pursue prevention. First-aid fixes can often save the day, but many times it is only after great effort, expense and emotional energy have been expended.

In the spirit of preventive management, here are a few things we've discovered. You old timers have discovered which of these things are important for your operation, you newcomers need to know them too.

Give your maiden does adequate time to develop. There seems to be no hard and fast rule but a little patience may be rewarded with a healthier dam and possibly twins instead of single births. It seems there is a general philosophy in goating that says does can be bred to kid at one year, or worse, 150 days after weaning. We've been successful breeding eight month old Spanish does to Kiko bucks and getting generally one healthy kid. However, after a kidding experience with a large number of yearling straight Spanish does bred to Spanish bucks, I have come to rethink that strategy. I've heard it argued that it is economically impractical to hold does until the next breeding season. But if you crank in the losses that will inevitably come plus the factor of single births, as opposed to kidding twins at 17 or 18 months, it appears that perhaps all one is giving up by waiting is sleepless nights and a poor financial return.

Weight is probably more critical than age and some experts suggest an 80 pound minimum for breeding doelings. Although does can be "pushed" with a feed bag to grow quickly to a breeding weight before the age of one year, there are drawbacks to this type of management beyond cost.

There is the risk of developing a portly doe that has laid excessive fat around her reproductive organs and in her udder. This can interfere with her fertility and her milking ability. We believe a more sustainable approach is the better route. We try to keep our does on quality forage, usually a browse and pasture mix.

Make sure that your vaccinations are up to date. Ask your vet what the problems are for your area. I've met folks who don't vaccinate and have no apparent problems. Their philosophy runs with the "if it ain't broke, don't fix it school." Sometimes that is a cost-effective approach, but when it comes to "over-eating disease" and "tetanus", it's probably not worth risking. The cost of a wreck will make one rue the day the decision to vaccinate was foregone. CD/T shots are cheap and effective. I once heard a goat horror story involving a goat rancher who was doing many things well but had missed the part of the information loop about CD/T. His vet was not a goat specialist either. He lost nearly fifty head of valuable kids and does to over-eating disease.

We believe that boosting the vaccinations in our does thirty days before kidding will allow some colostral immunity to be passed to the kid. We try to administer our first kid vaccination at two months of age when we think the immunity passed from the dam is declining and not high enough to interfere with the vaccine. This is soon enough to protect the kid without interfering with the colostral protection. The kid's vaccination is then boosted at weaning.

Be aware that parasites can be terrible during wet, relatively warm, winters. Check with your vet about doing fecal counts and which drenches are being used effectively on goats in your area. There are reports of parasites in certain areas becoming immune to dewormers. If this is true in your area, you might consider trying "DE" – diatomaceous earth – as another tool to help reduce the parasite load. Although some people disagree and most evidence in favor of it seem to be anecdotal, we have found dietary *food grade* diatomaceous earth to be a great help in avoiding heavy infestation and reducing the need for expensive, chemical fertilizers.

Observe the condition of your goats. Is the hair coat rough looking? If so, it could be parasites. Check the color of their gums, the mucous membranes under their eyelids and inside the vulva of the does. They should be pink; white could indicate serious anemia from blood sucking internal parasites.

Adequate nutrition, without overfeeding, is necessary to maintain the pregnancy and the health of the does and the kids. The last trimester is the most critical time of the pregnancy because most of the fetal growth takes place during these six to eight weeks.

Make sure that the protein levels are met and minerals and micronutrients are being supplied. Most of us will have to feed some supplement unless quality winter pasture and browse is available. Goats are fierce foragers. Even when it looks like the dead of winter, they will find quite a bit of good winter greenery if allowed the chance to be a goat. More than one producer has been surprised to find that his 'neglected" group of winter goats, left out in the brush and timber to forage most of their meal, look much better than those that were kept up in pens and fed.

We try to always keep a good loose mineral available. Our preference is Moorman's high copper mineral. It's been our experience that a good mineral with sufficient copper will totally eliminate footrot. We have gone through wet winters without a case of footrot in either the cattle or the goats when we've been diligent keeping the high copper mineral available. That's our testimonial to a high quality, high copper mineral. Check with your goat and forage specialist to find out what minerals are deficient in your area.

Don't forget the needs of your soil. In many areas, lime is more critical than fertilizer. Adjusting the soil pH, by adding lime, will free up available nutrients that can then be harvested by your goats. Lime, unlike anthelmintics, will feed your soil in a way that increases the growth of microbes and other soil life. Take care of your soil and a healthy pasture will take care of your critters.

We are learning that if we'll pay attention to these basic points, an ounce of prevention really is worth a pound of cure...and a whole lot more in peace of mind.

CHAPTER FIVE

How to Pick a Herd Sire

W hen breeding time arrives, putting the buck out involves a little more thought than just opening the gate. There are a few decisions to be made, but less than voting for a presidential candidate. After all, if your buck is promiscuous, courts doelings who are too young, avoids combat and doesn't inhale his nasal aerosol, you can still feel confident that he'll keep his promise to be the buck you believed him to be.

Everyone enjoys owning an outstanding looking animal and most folks do their best to select the best animal that they can afford. However, before taking the trip to the buck pen, it might be wise to consider the goals of your breeding season.

Take a good look at your does. Make a list of the traits that your does deliver and the ones which you would not be inclined to give up. List their perceived shortcomings as well. Next look at these pros and cons in the light of what you plan to do with the upcoming kid crop.

All are the kids going to slaughter? If so, you will need a "terminal sire" to give you the most desirable carcass. You might want to select a heavily muscled sire such as some of the Boer or Tennessee Meat Goats. If you buy a buck for a terminal sire, you might do well to remember that was your goal when it comes time to wean the kids. Keeping replacement does out of heavily muscled sires is sometimes disappointing. Muscle is a masculine trait and inversely related to the more feminine, maternal traits such as easy kidding and heavy milking. It is rarely possible to have both extremes in the same animal. On occasion, it happens, but often at the price of a high maintenance animal that will melt under commercial conditions.

Are you building a herd and planning to keep most of the doelings? If so, you will need to balance the traits of your does against those of your buck. If you need stronger maternal traits, select a buck from an outstanding doe. If possible ask to see the dam of the buck you are considering. Ask about her production history. Has she kidded every year, having at least twins? Has she raised at least twins to an acceptable weaning weight at approximately 100 days every year? Check the structure of her udder. High and tight with ample milk is the ideal. Pendulous udders that swing or drag are an invitation to injury and subsequent disease. Like begets like so don't discount the importance of the history and conformation of your buck's dam. Although our present thrust is to infuse as much Kiko into our does as possible, we believe the Kiko/Boer cross holds a lot of promise. The Kiko mother is an aggressive maternal force with a generous milk supply for her offspring. Kiko does are rarely victimized by dystocia even when kidded as yearlings.

Wethers from a Kiko buck will not be shabby either so using a Kiko buck on your commercial herd could be a balanced choice for you. An alternative sire which promises to offer both the kidding ease of the Kiko and the muscle and markings of the Boer is the Texas Genemaster. This is a certificated, registered composite breed, which is 5/8 Boer and 3/8 Kiko. There are a couple of ways of arriving at the final Genemaster cross which begins with registered fullblood Kikos and fullblood Boers. One which is popular among people with registered Boer females is to purchase a certificated Genemaster 3/4 Kiko 1/4 Boer buck. The resulting get is the Texas Genemaster, the intent of which is to combine the best of both worlds.

In the past, kids with the Boer marking have had an advantage at the local sale barn. Although the auction barn is usually our last-choice marketing option, there may be times when you must take your wethers to town and take the price they have to offer. Unless and until there is more recognition of the Kiko carcass, which has high cuttability, the producer may not believe he is being compensated fairly for his Kiko wethers which may look similar to a good Spanish goat. However, keep in mind, that higher kidding rates and number of live kids weaned may more than off-set this present discrimination while allowing the producer to also bene-fit by retaining replacement does. As marketing channels develop, Kiko producers will find buyers and processors who give new meaning to value added marketing with Kiko carcasses.

Libido is worth noting if you have a large number of does or wish to have your kid crop all born during a short interval. A lazy breeding buck could set your plans back. Overly conditioned bucks will have to expend more energy moving that extra weight around. Try not to be too impressed by fat, pen-fed goats. Fat, feed test bulls always sell first at the bull sales. They look beautiful and yet their semen tests are often the worst. The leaner, hard finished, grass raised bull may not get the billing of those fat and sassy bulls, but more often than not they prove to be more fertile and exhibit more stamina on the job. This line of reasoning should hold true for bucks as well.

If you are a commercial producer, be sure to keep your focus on pro-duction traits. Some attributes or traits may only have cosmetic signifi-cance although breeders may hype them as important. Try to do some research on the breed you are considering before buying. Check the breed standards as well as any general goat research you can find on conforma-tion and important production traits.

One item that seems to be much ado about nothing is the issue of split scrotums. Although I would prefer to see no split, I can find no statistical-ly significant evidence that a small split is any kind of problem. Rather, I find testimonials from large breeders around the world confirming that it is only a cosmetic issue. Some people speculate that a buck with a split scrotum will sire doelings with undesirable udders. Interestingly enough, even in the dairy breeds where the udder conformation is of primary importance, there is no discount to a buck with a small slit in the scrotum.

I would avoid using a buck with a low hanging, wildly swinging scro-tum since it could be a possible hazard in the brush. An injury during breeding season could have a serious economic impact on the farm's prof-itability. Other traits may not have economic significance but are worth noting from a management viewpoint.

Disposition is one that comes to mind. Both extremes can be problem-atic if your management style does not accommodate them. Two hundred fifty to three hundred pound bucks that are either extremely docile or extremely wild could present problems. When selecting a buck, keep in mind how your facilities will handle the movement of a mature buck. Will you or a hired hand be responsible for the routine health and pro-phylactic vaccination or de-worming? Do either of you have reservations or physical limitations when it comes to handling the large bucks? Will young children be around the buck, with or without permission, unsu-pervised at any time?

Although disposition may be a minor part of the decision equation, it is worth a moment's consideration. Our New Zealand import, Moneymaker, has the most docile disposition of any goat we've seen. Going on ten years of age, he's still an eager breeder and yet can be easily handled at working time. Kikos in general are a little more standoffish which I attribute to their survival instincts. Boers are known for their wonderful dispositions and this, we have found, is generally true.

Last, but not least, unless personally acquainted, check out the reputa-tion of the breeder from whom you are considering purchasing an animal. Make sure you have heard something good from somewhere besides his personal paid advertising. It will be worth your time and the cost of a few telephone calls to talk to more than one person. Call the breed associa-tion. Ask them directly if there's been any complains filed against the breeder you are considering. Even if they are not free to discuss the details, you may be alerted if there's been a history of problems with a particular breeder.

There are many things to consider when buying or choosing a buck, however, with a little homework now, you'll enjoy the result both next spring and in the coming years.

CHAPTER SIX

Kidding Time

I 'm not big on giving veterinary advice of any kind. I have always
believed that people should write about what they know. So, without
infringing into the veterinary arena, here's a brief rundown on what
we do on Caston Creek to get ready for kidding.

The first thing we do is retain does with a maternal edge. The second
thing we do is try to optimize the health of our does by whatever proactive and prophylactic means available to us. After that, we let the goat
moms take care of the kidding. With that preface, we proceed to order
some emergency kidding supplies. Just in case.

For the most part, I'm not going to tell you what to do with all of these
supplies because most of the kids that have required heroic measures to
save didn't make it. So that means one of two things. Either I am incredibly inept at kidding triage or the kids that needed help were beyond any
hope of surviving. I tend to think it was the latter, but I won't discount
other possibilities. As we continue to select heavily for tough mothers and
easy kidding, it is becoming a very rare event that a doe cannot raise her
own kids. Culling heavily for good mothers is probably the best thing you
can do to prepare for the next kidding season. Nevertheless, you never
know when it might be helpful to have some things on hand.

We keep some of those Pritchard Teats on hand just in case we need to
bottle a kid. They are easily screwed onto a pop bottle. It's a lot easier than

pulling that stiff black plastic nipple over one edge of the bottle only to have it pop off the other side while the base of the bottle skids out from under you spilling half of its contents. If a very young doe has triplets, we might consider removing one and bottling it. This would allow the young doeling to do a better job raising the remaining twins and still have a chance to continue growing herself.

We make sure there is some lamb replacer on hand. If we don't bottle baby goats, it can be used when one of the livestock guardian dogs whelp. Once the pups are on the ground, we feed the mother puppy chow with lamb replacer. The pups are soon joining her at the table and everyone stays in top condition. Additionally, the pups will be large enough to wean a little early if necessary. If we do begin bottling a kid, we try to stay with the same brand of milk replacer. We like the one Merrick makes and it can always be ordered through one of the goat supply catalogs listed at the end of this chapter.

If it becomes necessary to bottle kids, we add one teaspoon of Agri-Safe DE to the milk replacer that goes in each eight-ounce pop bottle. Bottle kids are susceptible to cocci and we've found that the small amount of dietary grade DE helps to protect them. DE is diatomaceous earth, a non-toxic, bio-product that is FDA/USDA approved as a food additive for anti-caking, has proven to be helpful to many producers.

We also ordered a bag of 0.9% Sodium Chloride. It can help a kid that is dehydrated and weak. Our vet told us how to administer it under the skin. Check with your vet before trying this. This year we also ordered some Goat Nutri-Drench to have on hand. We've heard people talking about it for years so we thought it ought to be in the emergency kit. We really don't know if it's all it's cracked up to be and, hopefully, we won't have to find out. So far it has stayed in the supply kit with the strapping tape over the pump just the way it was shipped. Those Kiko newborns are up and bumping pretty quickly so we haven't had a chance to see if it will help a weak kid yet. We also order a box of clean 20 gauge needles so we can always have a sharp, clean needle when needed.

We make sure we have the larger 140-ml syringe and the red rubber tubing that fits on it. If necessary, colostrum or milk can be milked directly into the syringe with less waste and administered immediately to the kid. We ordered the red tube because it is more flexible and less likely to injure the kid than the clear tube that is available. We also like to use the gravity flow method and avoid forcing the milk into the kid with a plunger. Be sure to tip the kid's head up while inserting the tube to avoid pushing it into its lungs and drowning it. Gently hold your finger against its throat and you will feel the tube as it passes to the stomach if you have it in the right place.

We believe it is important to use 7% iodine on the newborn's navel. A new wet umbilical cord can wick up bacteria and kill a kid. We have used it in a spray bottle and we have used the navel cup for dipping the cords. Either way, I seem to get it on me. You'll just have to try them both to see which one you prefer. The navel cup can be hung from a steel panel. If you are kidding in pens, that might be handy. We find ourselves tromping through the woods looking for new kids so a spray bottle in the supply bucket travels better.

Although that about does it for our Kid Emergency Kit, before kidding begins, we order eartags. We use a color and number system. The first digit of the tag will reflect the year the kid is born. 1999 year tags will start with the digit "9". We will have red tags for Boer goats, white for Genemasters, purple for Fullblood Kikos and orange, green, and blue for the percentage Kiko. It helps us to identify our kids at a glance. Later, it helps us identify our replacement does.

Kidding season can be a very exciting and satisfying time. But, it can also turn into a very stressful time for all if the kids don't survive and thrive. We learned pretty quickly that mopping up problems is costly, time consuming and inordinately stressful on the producer, not to mention the animal.

When we kid in the timber we set up a temporary facility. We designate a spot between the hills and ravines as the "facility area". We put up steel panels, feed troughs, and ring the outer perimeter with combination hay and mineral feeders. We supplement with alfalfa hay and a little corn, keeping the DE, mineral and kelp mixture available at all times.

Scattered around the fringes of the facility are some Port-A-Huts with kidding benches inside and some outside. When the weather is fair the does find shelter under a cedar tree or near a thicket. If it turns inclement, then the portable shelters provide cover for the does and their newborns. However, if a doe should kid in especially bad weather (wet and very cold), then we like to be prepared for that possibility by having a pen or two set up in a barn with a heat lamp. We hope we won't have to use them but sometimes a twenty-four hour visit to a friendlier environment can make the difference between success and failure.

Check your shelter options. Whether you are kidding in the brush or in the pasture, the same basics apply. Wind, wet and cold can be killer, especially to newborn kids. Make sure there is a place for them to escape the elements. Common sense will tell you a little six to eight pound mammal cannot generate enough body heat to keep warm in extreme wet and cold weather. Hypothermia can be a kid killer.

Kidding benches inside a shelter offer practical protection for young kids. Throw a little loose hay or straw under the benches and the kids will cuddle up to keep warm, protected from being smothered by the larger does. Sawdust or wood shavings make good bedding material. They can be easily cleaned out of the sheds in the spring and allowed to compost before spreading on your pasture or garden area.

Here's another management tip carried over from our days of calving heifers. If we feed our supplement late in the day, most of the does will kid during the morning or midday. That small management choice has probably saved a lot of kids that might have perished at night, especially when a cold wind was blowing. During the warmer daylight, with a little sunshine to help, they do just fine.

Last, but not least, always kid in clean pastures. A pasture which has had sufficient time to lay fallow without grazing animals impacting it daily will have time to recycle manure, compost some of the underlying thatch and allow air and sunshine to kill pathogens. Our focus is proactive rather than reactive. We believe that the animal's health is increased every time we increase the level of health in the pasture.

We have learned to avoid overstocking. We have learned the benefit of resting our paddocks and practicing intensive rotational grazing. We are learning the benefits that are derived from feeding the microbes in the soil with additives such as lime and organic fertilizers that don't kill the soil life. We have learned the benefit of addressing the micronutrient needs of the goatherd, both through the soil and with supplementation. We have learned the benefit of diatomaceous earth and the avoidance of unnecessary chemical deworming. No one thing is a cure-all, but all together they combine to increase the overall level of health in the herd. We like the holistic approach that looks at the big picture and considers more than just traditional, chemical oriented management.

We try to use this type of approach with kidding. We are realistic about the likelihood of some loss when population numbers are high. We know that all the vagaries of nature cannot be avoided but some things are in our control. We can do those things that will help to maximize our animal's health and benefit the kidding season.

*This good Spanish doe pulls
her weight on Caston Creek.*

*Freshly kidded Kiko Triplets are up
and on their way to the udder in minutes.*

CHAPTER SEVEN

Kikos Have a Maternal Edge

Ⅰt's said, "man is a political animal". Whether it's baseball teams or goats, people tend to get emotional over whatever they have chosen as the best. They also tend to be selective about what they are ready to defend. After all, there's only so much emotional energy to go around. I get emotional about my husband, my grandchildren, my children and my Anatolian Shepherd guardian dogs. As far as the goats go, they are just business.

Now, before anyone goes and gets all offended by that statement, let me say this: I enjoy those goats with the best of you. It's therapeutic for me to walk through the herd, to sit on a log or rock and watch them graze and see the kids scamper up and down off the highest spots they can find. It's satisfying to see the results of breeding choices and to watch the youngsters grow into fine adults. But, when it comes to which breed is the best, well, it's just a business decision for us. We need the animals that will work the best for us.

People always ask us why we chose to raise Kiko goats. The answer is really very simple. We approached the goat business with the same wide-open embrace with which we entered the cattle business.

We had no family favorites or peer group pressures to influence our decisions. Rather, we were driven by the same criteria used when selecting the breed of cattle we eventually settled upon. We were interested in production traits, not showring considerations.

While building the ranch, we had gravitated to a lifestyle of working away from the farm in order to earn the bigger bucks than were available in rural America. We found ourselves in the old catch-twenty-two situation. In order to make the capital investment we desired on the farm, we had to take jobs away from home.

Since we were not at home around the clock, the livestock could not require 24 hour per day supervision. That ruled out cattle with a history of calving problems. We solved that with the large pelvic girdles and small newborns of Salers Beef Cattle. Salers also forage well and have a hardy constitution. We wanted these same traits in whatever goats we bought.

Not knowing one goat from another, it seemed obvious that we should try several. We bought straight Spanish, Spanish/Boer crosses, Spanish/Cashmere crosses, and fullblood and percentage Boer and Kiko goats. By the time our numbers rose to six hundred some goats and we had three kidding seasons under our belt, we decided that the Kiko Goat was living up to the claim of being an early maturing, fast growing, fiercely maternal, and extremely hardy animal.

The Kiko goat was developed in New Zealand using a base of feral goats. The feral population in New Zealand had become huge because there are no natural predators for goats and as a result they were destroying forests. The government set about to capture thousands of the goats. Some forward thinking individuals used the opportunity to select a group of goats that would become the base for developing the Kiko goat. Under a scientifically designed program, the feral goats were crossed with outstanding Saanen and Nubian sires to set both milk and additional frame while retaining the traits of survivability and hardiness. Centuries of running wild had imbued the feral goat with many traits that favored commercial production. Slow hoof growth, parasite resistance, fierce mothering, good fertility and high libidos are some of the traits perpetuated.

At Caston Creek Ranch the critters find us to be an equal opportunity employer. That is, as much as possible, everyone is treated the same. They get the same vaccinations, feed and mineral supplements — all the same perks. At times the commercial goats (mostly Spanish crosses) had a nutritional edge since they were allowed access to the more remote, predator prone habitat that is also goat heaven in terms of forbs and browse. They enjoyed the smorgasbord of nature's plenty, while our faithful Anatolian Shepherds guarded them. Now we run all the does together so the more valuable goats can get the good stuff too. We are willing to risk some loss in order to maximize their health. However, even when the Kikos did not have the edge of the better browse, they were out performing everything on the place.

Every time we finish our spring kidding we discover that we've seen the Kiko does birth and wean more kids than any of the other breeds. They have what we like to call the maternal edge.

Kikos were developed under production criteria for the purpose of producing goat meat. To be profitable, the producer must have a doe that raises a fast growing kid to weaning. The developers of the Kiko goat believed that the ideal was to wean an acceptable weight at 100 days without having any input into the kid.

We believe it is important to continue the focus of the original developers to maintain and improve the original fertility, hardiness and vigor of the breed. With this in mind, one must ask if it is really desirable to breed for heavier weights at the cost of more kidding problems and higher mortality. Our goals are simple: we want a low maintenance animal with a high production history. In order to maintain some genetic diversity and take advantage of hybrid vigor, we are using different breeds of goats. One thing's for sure. If they expect to stay on the ranch, they will have to live up to the production standards set by the Kiko goats.

A well-conditioned buck
with sound feet and legs
can cover the terrain and
the does as well.

A mature Kiko stands guard over her newly kidded triplets.

CHAPTER EIGHT

Kidding Kikos
in the Timber

We kidded our Kikos in the timber again this year. We built and reinforced fence around 110 acres of heavily wooded terrain. Within its perimeter, the bottomland on the south rises into undulating hills, steep slopes and deep ravines on the north. There is a mixture of pine and oak, elm and hickory, persimmon and blackjack. Soon the arrival of spring will highlight the wild plum, cherry and huckleberry as the dogwood and redbud parade their flamboyant finery. Next the blackberry, honeysuckle and endless briars will make their debut along side other woodland flora and fauna.

Layers of rock protrude from the face of the hills and large slabs jut out to form convenient seats or handy ledges to tuck a kid beneath. Haphazardly these huge stones lie, jumbled in the creeks and at the bottom of ravines, making stair steps for springs that trickle into mini waterfalls.

This time of year the ground is covered with dried oak leaves and pine needles. Broken branches and pinecones nestle between the abandoned leaves forming Mother Nature's own potpourri. Dried bunch grasses stand in small golden clumps with tender green shoots peeking out of the old growth, teasing the passing grazer with promises of more to come.

Tiny purple flowers, sage colored lichens and fluorescent green mosses dot the ground and bare rocks. The morning sun quickly warms the southern slopes and we discover how goats prefer to handle kidding, when given the choice.

Years ago we were told that Kikos kid more like deer. We thought that was a charming sentiment but gave it no further thought. Before long we began to utilize the timbered areas of the ranch better. Each year we got a little braver about where and how to handle the kidding. We became convinced fairly early in the game that if you have strong mothers and you truly have confidence in their maternal ability, then you could let your goats do what comes naturally. That may be a big disappointment for folks who like to keep a huge amount of veterinary supply on hand or enjoy playing doctor. But for those who prefer to enjoy the miracle of birth and let nature take its course, it is delightful.

Papa and I have spent many enjoyable hours hiking through the timber looking for new kids to weigh and tag. This year was especially satisfying as we began to see the hard work and ruthless selection of previous years pay off. Even our yearling does kidded unassisted and displayed good mothering skills. Beyond the satisfaction of seeing the maternal edge engage with full force, we learned some new things about goats kidding in the timber.

Goats *are* more like deer than cattle. When the doe's time arrives, she will find a spot that is well protected from the wind, perhaps near the base of several large trees or under the spread of a red cedar's canopy or behind a fallen log, where the ground is clean and dry and previously undisturbed. The doe will kid, clean and suckle her offspring and rest. Then after some period of time, longer for some than others, she will put the kid down and go off to graze. Sometimes she will be seen rejoining the herd for several hours, returning later to suckle the kids, but often she stands a solitary vigil. Dawn and dusk seem to bring an urgent need for reunion as does call kids and kids return the call.

We also discovered the hidden nursery networking system that the does establish. They often lay up their babies in a newborn nursery, leaving one or two mothers as babysitters while the others go off to find some groceries. Our hearts skipped a few beats before we realized this was happening. We had several known-to-be excellent mothers come into the temporary facility showing signs of having kidded but without the kids in tow. At first we feared the worst - predators. So, we added a fifth guardian dog. As if wild dogs, bobcats, and coyotes weren't bad enough, we had seen eagles circling. The bald eagle aerie located at nearby Lake Wister generates a degree of uneasiness for us when kidding season approaches.

It was not long before we stumbled into one of the hidden nursery areas. Located on a grassy knoll above a steep rise, soaking up the sun in the cool spring air, were the mothers and their missing kids. Babies napped and mommies munched, a more peaceful or bucolic setting would be hard to imagine.

There are drawbacks to kidding in the timber. Certainly it would not be the premier choice for those with pet goats. Some losses are inevitable. Unfriendly forces lurk in darkened forest shadows and baby goats will disappear. An inexperienced yearling may wander too far and place her kids outside of the protective reach of the overworked livestock guardians. But, the kids will not be dying from breaches in the sanitation threshold of your goat operation and you won't spend time, emotional energy or sleepless nights nursing sick kids only to see them succumb after all. It's not for the faint of heart and like most of life, it has its tradeoffs.

Losses will be greatly reduced by kidding first time does in a more confined area where you can supervise them. Like first calf heifers, they are often at a loss to what is going on. They are inclined to wander too far, hide their kids, sometimes forgetting where, and lose them to predators. Our experience showed us that the mature does knew just how far they could go into the timber to kid and still be under the protected umbrella of the guard dogs on patrol.

The only downside to this kidding season, that Papa could see, was the purchase of some frozen dinners to save time that could be spent walking the woods looking for new kids. I found one entree that read like mama's homemade cooking – turkey and broccoli in gravy with dressing to boot. Papa thought it looked more like dog food with croutons on top. I had to agree. Tomorrow I'm packing peanut butter and jelly so that we won't have to return to the house for lunch. Instead, we can sit on a rock and watch the leaves open as spring sneaks in with an early symphony while does drop kids in the timber.

PART THREE

Practical and Proactive Management

An offset hot wire was added to this barbed wire.

Goats with clean water and good browse will thrive.

CHAPTER NINE

The Seven Habits of Highly Effective Goat Ranchers

We live in an era of self help resources. There are periodicals, newsletters, books, videos and seminars covering everything from gardening to grieving. It's the American Way – we can fix it ourselves. The authors of the quick fix, and even the not so quick fix, often have their message in a formula, nailed down to a precise number of tenets. AA has twelve steps, Deepak Chopra says there are seven steps to spiritual success and Stephen R. Covey claims that highly effective people have seven habits. It seems to me that highly effective goat ranchers must have something in common.

Habit #1

Keep the faith. Have a vision. Dream the dream. Know where you are going and what you hope to accomplish. Customize your vision to fit your personal life style and its requirements. If esthetics are important to you, be sure to include plans for that as well or you won't be happy if everywhere you look, you find that you have met your goals but created an eyesore for yourself.

Some of the experts say we should design a mission statement. This is a written statement defining your goals and purposes. It's hard to get where you want to go if you don't know where it is. Committing our dreams to paper helps us define the scope of our operation and the purpose we believe it serves. If a husband and wife are both saying "yes, we want to raise goats when we retire," but the husband is thinking "I'll take our savings to buy 2,000 commercial goats and the adjoining acreage so I'll have a full-time job when we retire," and the wife is thinking "won't it be nice to travel, remodel the house and have a few pets to take care of on our two acres..", there is more than an obvious collision course building here. The road maps that each of them has for their future plans are different and they will be making assumptions and decisions in the present based on different paradigms.

Habit #2

Plan ahead. Only when we know where we are headed, can we plan the route. Farming and ranching are full of daily interruptions. I've spent most of my life being a list maker. I found out pretty quickly that on the farm tomorrow's list of things to be accomplished has a slim chance of being finished. If a piece of equipment isn't breaking down, an animal needs tending, or the creek is up and we can't get across to finish a chore. The real secret is to not let the daily interruptions distract us from the big picture.

If we always drop what we are doing to fix the squeaky wheel, then sometimes we can lose sight of something more important that needs to be done. Before we know it, we keep putting off the important issues by tending to all the daily little nuisances.

Designing an annual plan, based realistically on the time and money we should have available to us, we can forecast the amount of progress we hope to accomplish by year's end. Sometimes, it helps to also have a two, three or five year plan. This can be helpful when we are projecting an increase of our breeding herd based on retained females. We will be able to figure the period of time and the approximate costs of raising the does as well as when we will realize the first income from this investment.

Finally, planning should include a drought management plan. If you've been comfortably grazing your place for a few years without a drought, you may be running close to a full stocking rate. Think about what your alternatives would be in a worse case scenario. The more paddocks you have to rotate through, the better off you'll be when a drought comes. If the very worst possible drought hits, can you dry lot your animals and feed them hay? Do you have an extra year's worth of hay put up to cover that eventuality? Not many do. Would you be better off to sell your animals at give away prices? These are not pleasant things to think about, but if we have an alternative plan, it can often buffer the ill effects.

Covey tells us to be proactive. This means take positive control. Let your actions be driven by your choices and decisions and your responses be fashioned by your beliefs and opinions. Try to avoid reacting in a knee jerk fashion to the agenda of others and life's daily interference.

Habit #3

Prioritize. Defining the dream and planning the route are sound steps but sometimes things don't go as quickly as one hopes. If there are several projects to be accomplished over the coming year, prioritize them in case there is a set back. Then you will have tackled the most important ones first. Prioritizing can also keep us from reacting to a crisis by throwing money at it. Sometimes it's better to take the longer, perhaps, more painful route through a crisis than to spend a lot of money trying to fix it. The unplanned outlay of capital may set back your planned expenditures unless you have prioritized them. You may be tending to a less important issue because it has your attention while sacrificing progress toward your goals.

Habit #4

Remember to be a grass farmer as well as a stockman. Good fences and good forage are among the keys to success. You don't even have to be an expert in intensive grazing to see the benefits of moving your livestock through several rotations. The plant diversity and improved herd health that results is obvious. Different plants access different nutrients. The varying depths of their roots pull up different minerals and your animals will show the effect of the so-called salad bowl grazing.

Cleaner pastures are an additional benefit. As the microbes and subsurface life increases, the manure piles will be quickly broken down and returned to the soil.

There are many books and publications available to help you learn to be a better grass farmer. If you are not already familiar with "The Stockman Grass Farmer", I suggest you get a subscription. (For a free sample, 1-800-748-9808).

Habit #5

Stay on top of potential parasite problems. You may have to schedule a strict drenching and vaccination program or you may find that rotation through clean browse and pasture areas with the addition of DE is all you need. This is definitely one area where it's far better to be proactive than reactive.

Goats probably don't need a lot of vaccinations compared to cattle, but they do need to be parasite free and that means you must be observant. Benign neglect could catch you with a wreck on your hands. Some people prefer drenching with a clear or white dewormer, saving Ivomec as a last line of defense. Even with the help of modern anthelmetics, more and more producers are encountering parasites that are becoming resistant to existing chemicals. Keeping an open mind will allow you to try some alternative health options that may make a big difference n your bottom line. Hopefully, in time, some bloodlines will be identified that are parasite resistant.

Habit #6

Use the best buck affordable. Remember fifty percent of your herd's genetics come from that one animal. Pedigrees are important and can be impressive but, if you don't like the way the buck looks, don't rely on his pedigree to give you what you want. Like begets like.

Habit #7

Take time to renew yourself. Remember while we are working toward our goals that all we ever really have is the journey and the present moment. So, take time to watch the goats play, to count your blessings, to talk to the Man Upstairs, to appreciate the wonder of life, and to feel joyful. Papa's father, ol' Doc Tomlinson, always said, "It's a great life, if you don't weaken."

CHAPTER TEN

Stress Reduction: A Holistic Point of View

They're everywhere! They're everywhere! Bugs! You know, the bad guys – germs, bacteria, parasites, crud, molds, funguses, and viruses that fly in on an ill wind. They are out there waiting to strike. You get the post holiday flu or sinus infection and your goat gets pneumonia or footrot. "How come?" you say. You are doing everything the same. Why should the bugs get you one time and not another?

Well, chances are it hasn't been *exactly* everything as usual when you or your animal gets sick. Just as you find yourself subjected to the holiday stresses of late nights, rich foods, that extra cocktail, or worrying about exceeding the Christmas budget, your goats can face some extra stresses too. These stresses can all take a toll on the immune system of the animal.

Holistic Veterinarian, Richard "Doc" Holliday, of Waukon, Iowa, says, "I think we give germs way too much weight as the cause of problems. My guess is that a germ can't tell if an animal is dead or alive…but if an animal is so *stressed out* that it *tastes* dead to the bacteria, they immediately begin the recycling process. In dead animals we call it decomposition...in a live animal we call it disease." This may be a new way of looking at things for some of us. Let's explore this avenue of thought a little more.

If the bugs are always out there, then the level of health enjoyed by the animal is a function of his ability to resist them. Dr. Holliday says, "Stress is known to lower immune function and may be the primary factor that sets the stage for animal disease." He states that there are three categories of stress.

1. Environmental or Physical Stress.

This can include anything that impacts the animal physically. Here's a list (you can probably think of some more things to add to it):

a) Poor Nutrition. Inadequate protein, especially during growing periods or gestation can create stress on the animal and the fetus during the last trimester. Mineral deficiencies can be insidious, in that the animal can appear healthy outwardly but is vulnerable to disease because it lacks proper levels of necessary trace minerals. (This is usually where I make my pitch for copper, cobalt and iodine for goats.) Minerals are a physical addition like food but they dramatically effect the physiological status of the animal. If the deficiency progresses beyond the subclinical level, the animal will appear unthrifty or become diseased.

b) Bad Water. Goats are much more particular about water than cows, but all livestock needs a clean source of water. New Zealand goat management consultant, Graham Culliford, has told me more than once that if I won't drink the water, don't expect my goats to drink it.

c) Sanitation. Too many goats in too small an area equal disaster. Parasite problems are only part of the potential problems that could be anticipated. Distress is increased as poor sanitation seems to encourage the proliferation of the bad bugs.

d) Weather Stress. We have no control over the weather but we can ameliorate its effect by having adequate shelter from wind and water (whether rain, snow or ice). Goats can handle a lot of cold as long as they can be out of the wind and stay dry.

e) Habitat. Not all environments are suitable for goats and some are definitely better than others. For instance, certain web-footed, long-eared Brahman cattle might inhabit a swamp with its alligator infested waters, but that's probably unsuitable for most goats.

f) Poor Hoof Maintenance. Some animals don't need much hoof care. They have slow growing hooves or they have hard, rocky surfaces to keep them worn down. Others, in soft pastures, wetter environments, and with a tendency to grow, will require more frequent trimming. If left undone, the hoof becomes deformed, the animal experiences physical discomfort and is impaired in his ability to get out and "hoof it" over to the forage bank.

First, address your animal's physical comfort. A goat does not require a heated barn, at least not in most parts of the world. He does need basic shelter from the elements, a clean area with access to clean water, feed, and ideally, forage.

In some situations, at some times of year, one might need to dry lot livestock and feed hay and feed. If so, take care that there is enough room to prevent overcrowding that can lead to poor sanitation and psychological stress. In such cases, the foodstuff needs to be off the ground. Don't pour pellets onto the ground. The goats will just pick up parasites along with the feed.

2. Physiological Stress

Physiological Stress is the second category that Dr. Holliday identifies. This is the type of stress associated with reproduction and lactation. Doc says, "We can minimize some of the effects of this type, but we cannot totally eliminate it."

We can remember to address their physiological needs, to some extent, by offering a good loose mineral. Our experience is that goats need copper, iodine and cobalt. We feed a Moorman high copper mineral. In the "Maximizing Minerals" section of the *FORAGE SAMPLER* newsletter (April 1998) by Kent Mills of Hermliegh, Texas, he says, "The need for copper begins when an animal is still a fetus in its mother. The highest requirement for a ruminant animal is during the late gestation period. For a cow, that's the last three months before calving. For a ewe or a nanny, it's the last four to six weeks prior to lambing or kidding.

The reason for the high need for copper at this time is that the amount of copper deposited in the liver of the fetus will determine how well it can respond to challenges to its immune system after it's born."

Kent continues, "Milk doesn't have a very high level of copper in it. That's one reason why the copper requirement of a lactating cow is not so high. It's also why a calf, lamb, or kid need copper in their liver at birth. The only appreciable amount of copper they will receive after birth is from the forages they eat. So if the copper level in the forages is low, the young ruminants will become deficient in copper in a few months. After that time, their immune system will not be able to respond as well to challengers from viral and bacterial organisms as when they have (a) normal level of copper."

Kent goes on to suggest that people obtain forage samples and get some baseline data on the mineral levels in their forages. He also advises to make sure that the copper in your mineral supplement is in the form of copper sulfate or a chelated form because, although copper oxide is cheap, it is unavailable to the animals.

Many people use kelp mixed with loose minerals to supply additional iodine. Dyed in the wool chemical advocates might look askance at this but real producers who have tried it all are finding that many natural alternatives have an advantage. Besides a source of iodine, kelp has numerous trace minerals that undoubtedly benefit goats and other livestock. Just because some chemical company has not funded the research on some aspect of Mother Nature's bounty, that does not void the effectiveness of it.

Cobalt (cyanocobalamin) can be obtained in a subcutaneous injection of B-12. We like to administer it whenever we handle the goats for vaccination, deworming with chemical wormers, or hoof trimming. New Zealand goat consultant Graham Culliford calls it a "magic tonic" for goats.

3. *Psychological Stress*

a) Change of group composition.

We see this type of stress when we wean kids or change the group composition for whatever management need we are facing. It will help to minimize stress by sorting some groups by age. Weaned bucks will probably do better if they don't have to compete with older bucks for space and feed. There are different management decisions that can be made, with regard to changing groups, that will help to eliminate some of the stress your animals face daily. You have probably noticed by now that goats, like cattle, will establish a pecking order when new animals are introduced or removed, or group structures are changed.

b) Handling Stress.

We also see this type of stress when handling animals. There is a wide range distress experienced by goats when handling. A goat that was raised on the bottle might handle you more than you could ever handle it. It seems those bottle babies never get over looking for some treat in your pocket. On the other hand, a nanny off the wide open Texas range might never get used to being too close to we two-legged critters. Goats that are stressed in late pregnancy can abort due to physical and/or psychological stress without any pathogenic involvement.

We reduce the number of times we must handle the goats by always mixing DE (food grade fresh water diatomaceous earth) with the feed and mineral. Our experience is that the DE dramatically reduces the frequency with which we must use toxic, chemical anthelmintics. (However, some recent research makes the claim that DE is not particularly effective in spite of the obviously reduced fly numbers in barn areas.)

c) Presdator Stress

Presdator pressure or harassment by another species presents another kind of stress. Whether coyotes, mountain lions or packs of domestic dogs on the loose, this can be a constant stress that may not always be obvious to the owner. We solve this problem by running several Anatolian Shepherd guardian dogs with our goats.

When we bring new goats to our farm or ranch, we can expect some adjustments to take place. That kind of move represents a major stress in a goat's life. A perfectly healthy animal is suddenly assaulted in three categories. First, he experiences *physical stress* while traveling. Physical stress is coupled with *psychological stress* – traveling over long distances, in crowded compartments, often without the safety net of his goat family only to land at a location full of foreign goats. Pretty stressful!

Finally, his physical distress may be compounded by the arrival in an environment that is totally alien from where he originated. The water, as well as the mineral and nutrient content of grasses and forages, may be different enough that the flora in his rumen will have to adjust to the new environment. That can take a couple of weeks. This places *physiological stress* on the animal. Assaulted on three fronts, the goat gets the famous "shipping fever", sort of like our sneezy, coughing, itchy, stuffy nose syndrome, which as far as I can tell is like coming down with a bug when you get run down. And like the flu, there can be secondary infections to follow. The bugs are all out there…just don't let down your guard!

So the big challenge, as I see it, is to stay on top of things by being as proactive as possible. In other words, instead of spending time, money and energy mopping up the damage of disease, an investment in prevention will pay off better. Part of this is maintaining an awareness of the stresses that assault your goat.

Doc says there are three levels of approach to livestock health. The lowest is the treatment of sick animals, the second is disease prevention and the third and highest level is health enhancement. From at least a prevention level, if not an enhancement level, there are several things we can do to insure that some of the stress is minimized.

It is important to look at all aspects of your animal's world along with the care you are giving in order to realize a high level of health in your herd. The whole picture is important. If we strive for a more holistic approach, the bugs will have a tough time taking us down.

CHAPTER ELEVEN

Good Fences
Make Life Easier

A decade ago, give or take a year or two, Papa and I attended a seminar on diversified agriculture in Henryetta, Oklahoma. One of the speakers was Dr. Frank Pinkerton, retired goat specialist, who is known as The Goat Man in the goat community. Frank uses words like an artist uses the paintbrush. His words leave pictures in your mind that make you remember what he's trying to tell you. He has said a lot of things that I'll remember about goats, but my favorite is that a good goat is sort of like pornography. It's pure hell to describe but easy to recognize. Another is that if your fences won't hold water, they won't hold goats. The more experience we have with goats and fences, the more I believe that truer words were never spoken.

About the time we thought we had the perfect set up, the goats got out. We had been successful for a couple of months in keeping the youngest group of does with a guardian dog, Babe, in a seven-or eight strand barbed wire fence. We always meant to run an offset hot wire but somehow we never got around to it. Babe, still a young dog, could get out by jumping through a gap about two feet off the ground where the wires were further apart or she could find a low spot and crawl under the bottom wire, but the does stayed in.

We didn't insist that Babe stay inside the four-acre pasture because we knew it was her nature, embedded in her DNA, to want to patrol the adjoining area looking for danger lurking. At least that was how we rationalized her unwillingness to always stay inside the fence. She wouldn't go far, sometimes only a few feet from the fence. She would lie in the dead Bermuda grass soaking up the afternoon sun while always alert, listening and watching her does. As in most relationships, there were two sides to the interchange between Babe and her does. Not only did the young Anatolian prefer to be with the doelings, they appeared to like having Babe close at hand.

The does began following Babe out of the pasture. Before long, in one graceful hop, they learned to jump between the fifth and sixth strands of wire like little deer. They'd continue right past where Babe was lying and head for the creek area. Babe would get up and trudge after them. Soon they would satisfy themselves with whatever winter forbs and grasses that could be found along the creek before moving on to the bull pasture and maneuvering past another seven-strand barbed wire fence. From there they crossed the county road and grazed the fescue in the yard of an abandoned house until a loaded coal truck came down off the mountain, shaking the ground, grinding gears and sounding like it was going to level the entire mountain in the process. I don't know whether Babe brought her girls back home in the face of a perceived threat or whether the sound of that metal monster frightened the little caprines. Regardless, they ran at top speed to the safety of their pasture.

We decided we couldn't have the does wandering off the property. The coal trucks had killed enough of the local residents so there was no expectation that they would stop for goats. We put the youngsters and Babe in a larger pasture, with brother Tex and the bred commercial goats. We thought the move to Myrtle's Pond Pasture (named for Papa's mother, Myrtle, who enjoyed fishing the pond in this pasture) would temporarily solve the problem of keeping the little does under control. Myrtle's Pond Pasture had a more secure fence line.

We had never had an escapee from Myrtle's Pond Pasture once the goats were trained to the hot wire. Occasionally, a goat that was unfamiliar with electric fence would hit the hot wire and, instead of pulling back, would bolt on through the fence. But, goats are smart and they don't make that mistake twice.

However, there was one stretch of fencing along the road coming into the house that was not hot. It was just a pretty good seven-strand barbed wire fence. So, of course, the little doelings exercised some positive transfer from their previous learning experiences with seven-wire fences and hopped right out. In their defense, they were confused by their new location and kept returning to their old home base, arriving to find the feed trough empty and the Port-A-Hut removed.

After a day or two the does seemed to accept their new home, but they were still sneaking off to foray into some new area, looking for winter's elusive greenery with Babe in tow.

We didn't worry too much because we thought they were staying on the ranch and Babe was one constant we could depend on, always vigilant, hovering like a new mother over her precious bundles. Some people have been known to cry at the beauty of an operatic solo. I find a similar beauty in Babe's devotion to the little four legged critters. They always came home but they were indiscriminant with regard to property boundaries and ownership. Still, their escapades seemed harmless enough until they ventured past the south line into the dreaded Forbidden Zone.

The Forbidden Zone is a weedy pasture adjoining our place that was used to graze cattle by a neighbor who years ago objected to our handful of goats that would occasionally venture over to eat the weeds. Evidently, nearly a decade later, he still had not learned the secret that goats will improve grass for cattle by eating the competing weeds that the cattle don't like. Some people have said goats can increase the grass by as much as 30% by eliminating the weedy scourge.

Inevitably, it had to happen. The does decided to visit the Forbidden Zone. We had men working on a new roof for the goat barn when they heard several shotgun blasts followed by birdshot raining down on the newly roofed barn.

It didn't take long to figure out what might be happening. Feed buckets were grabbed and a mad dash made to call the goats back through the little stretch of browse and timber that lies between the ranch and the Forbidden Zone. From there, the goats were led through a pasture and into some horse wire pens.

The nannies spent a few days going between the pens and a small but effective high tensile hot wire pasture while upgrades were put in place along Myrtle's Pond Pasture. We settled for an offset hot wire so that we wouldn't have to use Frank Pinkerton's recipe for a nine-strand barbed wire fence.

Frank says to keep goats in:

- run one wire on the ground to keep predators from digging in
- run the next three wires two notches apart on the t-post
- run two more wires three notches apart
- increase the distance between the wires to four notches and run three more wires. The T-posts need to be close together (ten to twelve feet) with twist stays every three feet.

Frank's fence is good and tight but we've found that a single offset hot wire works equally well for keeping the goats in *if* you can manage electric wire and insure that it will stay hot. For buck pens, we've found that one offset hot wire along field fencing works good too. They can't go through the netting and the hot wire keeps their horns out of it in case they try.

If a picture is worth a thousand words, I need to remember the picture in my mind of Frank Pinkerton's nine-strand barbed wire fences. There's a reason he's called The Goat Man.

CHAPTER TWELVE

Grass Farming and Drought Protection

I t seems to me, the older I get, that life has a way of serving up the
same lessons, time after time until we get it right. Sometimes we
know the right answers but walking the walk isn't always as easy as
talking the talk. It is true for learning to be a grass farmer first even
though your heart is with the goats.

It also seems to me that the basic premise of *grass farming first* is that
you capture the free energy of the sun by using your livestock to harvest
the forage that you have managed in a way that it will keep your animals healthy and growing. In turn this will allow them to gain and produce a desired number of pounds per acre to sell to provide you with a
profit.

If we are not careful, profits can dissolve in a sea of expense. Parasite
loads and hoof trimming are the nemeses of goat ranching. The cost of
anthelmintics and labor to administer the dewormers and to trim hooves
can erode profit pretty quickly, not to mention the wear and tear on the
producer. However, if goats are going to be raised in confinement, then
the inevitable reality is that there will be parasites and costly deworming
and hoof trimming.

Becoming a grass farmer first, rather than a stockman, may hold the key to success. The theory is great. It makes sense when we have too many weeds in the pasture or all that marginal land with forbs and browse that we should have goats to eat it! We read about grass farming, talk about it and then we buy our livestock and start trying to live it. The first thing we know, we've got a huge feed bill, vet bill, and we're worn out from having to work goats all the time.

Often the problems develop when we lose sight of some of the basics. Generally it seems to come down to losing sight of grass farming basics. If the sun is providing us with free energy that those little chlorophyll factories in plant leaves are using to generate more root, stem and leaf, then that means we are getting free food for our critters. That's true to the extent that we don't overstock and overgraze our pastures and browse areas. Sometimes we forget that and then we find ourselves throwing feed at our animals in order to keep their body condition. Also, the parasite zone in most pastures is four to six inches, eight inches in bermuda grass...graze it down below that and you'll be deworming more often. Purchased feed and anthelmintics equal diminishing profit.

One of the biggest mental traps to new ranchers is the idea that if they increase their stocking rate, they'll increase their profit. Too often more animals mean only more expense. Unless there is enough forage grown by the free sunlight to generously sustain them in a healthy manner, the profit won't be there. Goats are subject to crowding stress just like any other animal, especially when it creates intense competition for food.

Papa and I attended a goat field day one year at Prairie View A & M University in Prairie View, Texas. One of the most outstanding speakers was a young rancher named Kyle Clement who is making his living with goats. He was well educated, articulate and really didn't care whether he hurt anyone's feelings about the way that they ranched or not. He called it the way he saw it. He had a way of saying things that you might already know but to which you maybe weren't paying proper attention. One of those deafening statements was "every time you open a feed sack, you should be saying 'What am I doing wrong?'".

Kyle also touched on holistic approaches and going organic. He admitted that making the transition from traditional heavy fertilizer, high input farming requires *tough love*. Applied nitrogen creates an addiction in your grass and forage and reduces the ability of plants to get nutrients. It's not necessarily an easy transition and although the organic approach will be ultimately cheaper from a cash point of view, more management, especially THINKING management, will be required.

Kyle said you've got to be ready to look at a weed for awhile and certainly as goat ranchers we should be learning to look at weeds as choice goat forage. Kyle had some tips such as spend money on seed (especially legumes such as clovers, hairy vetch and Australian sweet pea) instead of nitrogen and overseed in the fall. By the third year you can cut your seed bill in half and plant Jose wheat grass and Marshall ryegrass. Oats are also a good winter feed. Try to have a monthly special available nearly year round. A varied cultivar will provide plants maturing at different times.

Rotating pastures and allowing paddocks to rest before introducing livestock does more than just let the grass grow back. It allows the plant root to dive deeper into the soil. In Joel Salatin's article "Generating Soil Fertility On Farm" in the May 1998 issue of ACRES USA, he reminds us that "what is below ground is a mirror image of what is above, therefore, grass plants constantly grazed or mowed short have extremely short roots. But plants allowed to grow longer have far more root mass." This larger root mass will more effectively access minerals and will also go deeper to seek moisture during times of drought. Then when the livestock mow the grasses and forbs to a shorter length, the deeper root mass will return to the soil providing tilth and more organic matter.

In recent years we have seen the El Nino effects play havoc with our farming and ranching plans. Destocking and cross fencing can provide a little drought insurance. This year may be a good time to stop sitting on the fence and to make a commitment to let goats be goats and to care for our soils in a more natural, environmentally friendly and easier on the pocket book manner.

This balanced young Kiko buck is a good choice for maiden does who will have an easier time kidding Kiko kids.

Even in a drought, goats can thrive when run under range conditions with plenty of browse available.

CHAPTER THIRTEEN

Blessings
in the Drought

During the early fall of 1998 it seemed as if it finally rained everywhere in Oklahoma, Texas and the great Southeast except on Caston Creek. The mountains, which routinely split storms and send them on around our banana belt, worked against us that summer. We were denied the rejuvenating rain that could start the healing of burnt grasslands and timbered areas. Eventually it came but before it did we found ourselves thinking about the positive things that had come out of the drought. We were fortunate to have dispersed 70% of our cow herd before the drought hit with a fury and knocked the floor out of cattle prices. Everything in life is a trade off of one kind or another. Massive culling left us with a premier set of bovines.

We didn't disperse the goats. With plenty of unexplored timber, we figured they would do what they do best. Up in the timber, the browse was heat stressed but plentiful and some shaded forbs and grasses remained with a trace of green. Picking their way though the scrub oak, hickory, red cedar and pine, selecting the most appealing morsel, the does remained fat and shiny. A feeder full of diatomaceous earth mixed with a high copper mineral remained in a handy spot at all times. Occasionally a sack of pelleted feed was sprinkled along the hot dry trail just to remind them that it's often worthwhile to come when called.

As summer began to wind down, the pastures were the color of wheat at harvest time. Most of them were eaten to within a couple of inches of the soil. We moved the cows to a new paddock knowing that if the rains didn't come, there would only be one move left. The rains didn't come in time and once they did the armyworms took what was left. We sold more cows, rationed the limited amount of winter hay and finally sent the remains of the herd to winter pasture in wheat country. While the future of the remaining cattle was uncertain, the goats' residency was not threatened.

The goats' forage requirements are more diverse. Although they can be managed on pasture, where they will first eliminate the weeds, they excel on browse, where they can show us what they do best. Goats readily convert forage growing on marginal, uncultivable lands to meat.

Since we try to see the rose rather than feel the thorn, here's some of the good things that we've learned come with a drought:

First, it's a great chance to sanitize the pasture. Parasites are not the only thing killed by hot dry weather. Last spring when I spoke with Dr. Jim Everman, virologist, Washington State University, I remember him telling me that a few days over 100 degrees Fahrenheit can kill a lot of viruses. We had weeks over 100 degrees and some days when the thermometers were hitting 112 degrees by late afternoon. It has been hot and dry for a very long time.

Second, a drought can provide the opportunity to dredge out silted ponds and watering holes. Goats like clean water. If your water source is a clear running stream or a spring-fed hole, a good drought may be the only time you see the water low enough to do some redesigning.

Third, if you are forced to cull animals, you will inevitably have a better herd when the deed is done. Selling off the low end can be difficult. Decisions can be painful when the favorites have to go. There may even be some guilt ridden moments of remorse when the critters are loaded into the trailer. However, if the culling criteria is based on production and not a sweet looking face or sentimental story, you'll come out the winner in the end. The drought forced us to make those tough decisions with our cattle and now we have one of the best sets of easy keeping bovines known to man. Before they went to winter pasture, we walked through what had become the heart of our herd and saw big fat mamas and their calves standing in patches of brown bermuda grass that looked deader than a round bale left in the field until late winter. We made similar decisions with the goats. It was harder to judge by their condition since they always managed to find a spot to graze but there was a low end and it went to the barn. The goat herd improved and those kind of results takes away the sting of deep culling.

Kids love to climb!

Zack finds a playmate on a kidding bench.

CHAPTER FOURTEEN

A Time for Every Purpose: Winter Planning

During the first week of 1998, we had over seven inches of rain pour onto our already saturated pastures. The creek was raging and muddy looking as it threatened to take out trees along its banks and any wimpy watergaps it might encounter. Endless winter days shrouded us with a gray dampness that left me feeling about as charged as a solar panel sitting under a bushel basket. There may have been a lot of potential there, but just no kick. Nevertheless, our livestock needed tending whether we thought we'd enjoy it or not, so Papa and I did our best to finish the chores and get back into the warm house.

When the days are sunny and inviting, I can find an endless list of tasks outdoors that need to be addressed. But during those wet and gloomy days, I was content to catch up on all those details of ranching that were pushed aside during fair weather, as "rainy day" work.

I found I could do things like plan our identification program for spring kids and calves. We settled on the Allflex medium tag for the kids.

It's easier to read than the sheep and goat tag but it stays in the ear just as well. We color code the tags for our kids according to the percentage of blood (whether Kiko or Boer or commercial) that they have in them and tag them at birth in ascending order. A quick glance at the tag gives us an idea of both breeding and the age of the kid.

It was also a good time to update inventory lists and prepare worksheets. I find I just can't work livestock without an up-to-date inventory checklist. I want to know *who, what* and *when*…who got what vaccine, de-wormer or treatment on which date. If we plan ahead we can think about what we wish to accomplish when we work livestock and make a check-off column for each job. For instance, once we decided to record weights on the ten month old Moneymaker bucks. They averaged around 85 pounds at six months so we were wanting to see if they had continued to grow as well on forage, a good mineral and a minimum amount of supplement. We like to hard finish our bulls and bucks. We believe it produces a more fertile animal.

We made our worksheet so that it contained columns for six month and ten month weights. If we hadn't thought about it ahead of time, we would have found ourselves in the field trying to hurry through this list of chores and forgetting to take their weights. It helps to have a written priority list in order to stay focused and not let the daily squeaky wheels get all the attention. Certainly, there are always adjustments to be made but we try not to lose sight of the overall big picture.

For us, pasture improvement and fencing is a number one priority. We continue to goat proof the perimeter of more distant timbered areas now that the dogs are big enough to pull their weight against a pack of coyotes or other predators. We managed to win the race to finish before spring kidding this year. We wanted to put the does on a clean hillside with the timber for shelter. We have learned that kidding Kikos only requires clean ground, browse and a few good guard dogs.

Winter can also be a good time to start planning the coming year's breeding program. Before the doelings are on the ground we are checking pedigrees and starting to think about the best mating possibilities for them. There's more time now for such ruminations than there will be once the grass is up and the weather is inviting.

Along with planning the next breeding season, winter is the time to be taking care of the pregnant does. It is worth the time spent to assess your plans for feeding your does in their last trimester. Protein is critical during this time. A good mineral is always imperative along with adequate protein. If the doe's nutritional requirements are not met in the last trimester, she can dump the pregnancy. That's one mistake along the learning curve that could permanently discourage a newcomer. Over 90% of the kids' growth occurs during the last 45 to 50 days of gestation. Inadequate nutrition can result in abortion or weak kids. No producer can afford feeding mistakes.

As part of a good nutritional program, whenever we work a goat we like to give an injection of "Maxi-B 1000". It supplies the critically needed cobalt in the form of B-12. It's worth the extra effort and something that should be standard fare in the goat herder's repertoire.

There's plenty to do indoors this time of year to keep busy but every winter I find myself pressing my face against the windowpane looking for the first hint of spring. When I tire of that, I find my way to the kitchen and throw together a little chevito mas fina. It's a good time to plan some meals around the new lean meat for the new millenium chevon, chevito, cabrito, call it what you will, but do yourself a favor and learn to cook it.

Just sitting in the mineral feeder observing the goats.

Zachary plays hide and seek with the new kids.

CHAPTER FIFTEEN

What the Devil *IS* Diatomaceous Earth?

Author's Note: This chapter appeared in the 1st *edition of "The Meat Goats of Caston Creek" and was reprinted later in* The Stockman GrassFarmer Magazine. *DE, as diatomaceous earth is often called, is a source of constant controversy. One study showed it to be something less than effective and as one goat farmer told me, people either swear by it or swear at it. Additionally, it can pose a breathing hazard if the fine silica like dust gets into one's lungs. Our experience with it in the humid SE Oklahoma summer time led us to believe it was beneficial for our operation. There was no question that it kept the fly population down in the barns and around the mineral feeders. That being said, I offer it again, this time with the caveat to use only food grade DE (not the swimming pool version), proceed with caution and make up your own mind.*

Here I am, again, sitting in the mineral feeder. It's one of those we made for the cattle – sturdy boards forming a broad base with closed ends and a low center of gravity to avert tipping and spilling the contents. It makes a perfect observation point. I can lean against one end while the corrugated tin shields me from the misty drizzle. Sometimes, at this hour of the morning, its roof keeps me from squinting as the sun makes its way from east to west, hugging the southern horizon now that the days have shortened. I make lazy circles with my finger in the soft loose powder and think about how one minor change in management has made a major change in our goat ranching operation. The change has been the addition of diatomaceous earth.

I had heard of diatomaceous earth, "DE" for short, in an organic gardening context over two or three decades ago. I didn't have a need for it at the time so I dismissed its claims, consigning the concept to a mental shelf for later evaluation. Now, so much later that it seems like another lifetime, we find ourselves raising goats and looking for ways to avoid the stress caused by sudden death, anemia, bottle jaw and frequent, expensive, chemical deworming of livestock.

There's an old adage "when the student is ready, the teacher is there". I guess we just had to get ready enough to learn something new because all of a sudden it seemed as if everywhere we went we were running into conversation about DE. We bought a few bags and figured we'd try it. The weeks went by and the goats looked good. We kept looking for signs that we should deworm but didn't see any indication that it was necessary.

We had one large-framed doe with triplets that was coughing and looking poorly after one particularly nasty, late spring rain. She was the only apparently sick one out of about 300 does. We took her into the vet. It turned out she had walking pneumonia and in the process of examining her, the vet took a fecal sample which returned a very low count. So low that at first he said it showed no eggs, then he corrected himself to be technically correct. I began to think there may be something to those DE claims. I thought this ill doe should have been the most susceptible to parasites if any of the goats were having problems.

More time passed and we still did not drench the goats. It wasn't that I had any great hope or confidence that the DE was working (although I was beginning to suspect it was) it was just that I was dreading the prospect of spending all day wrestling a huge number of goats. That was in the early summer. Then the drought hit with its unrelenting, dangerous temperatures and soaring heat indices. The goats were still looking okay. By August I was losing sleep – we had definitely gone too long without drenching. In late August we gathered the mob in from the timber, many still with kids at their side. We started to work them. The heat climbed rapidly and one doe expired in the corral nearly before we began. We decided that she was our canary in the mineshaft and if we didn't halt this foolishness there might be more dead goats, or worse yet, one of us with a heat stroke. We quickly sorted, turning does back out to the creek without deworming, handling only the kids for a quick prophylactic drench and weaning.

The summer wore on, the pastures dried up and the goats stripped the timber of browse, returning daily to the loose mineral and DE mixture. The cattle were showing some stress from the drought but the goats looked robust. In early September the rains came and all the critters nibbled close to the ground as things began to green.

Finally it was time to sort the does into breeding herds and haul them to the appropriate pasture to be romanced by the buck of our choice. This time we decided they must be drenched. I can't say that they needed it but most had gone the better part of six months without deworming and that was just too mysterious for me. Papa shook his head and figured I must have heard too much coffee shop talk that seems to say if anything can go wrong in agriculture, it will. It's not that I didn't believe the DE was working, the goats looked great. It's just that sometimes it's hard to learn new things.

DE is a management tool and to be used effectively it must be understood. It is not the Great American Goat Cure All. We Americans often want a simple, quick fix, one pill for an instant cure. DE requires observation and some thinking management. For us it has dramatically reduced the need for chemical dewormers. In some situations, where goats can browse above their shoulders, it may replace toxic chemicals entirely. In other situations, such as confinement, it will reduce infestation and increase the interval between expensive, traditional treatments.

Reducing the interval is just the tip of the iceberg as far as what is happening inside the goat. One thing that always bothered me about chemical wormers, besides the toxicity and stress on the goat, was that when dewormed on day number one, the same goat would b back in the pasture getting reinfested by day number two and continuing in that mode of reinfestation until the effects started to show outwardly about three weeks later. The poor goat never got rid of parasites.

The DE advantage is that it keeps the animal continually clean, or at least at a very low level of infestation, by being available at all times in a loose mineral mix. We mix it at a 40% DE to 60% mineral ratio. When we first began using it, we encouraged the goats to eat it by adding cottonseed meal at about a 20% by volume ratio. When sack feed is necessary, we add two pounds of DE to every fifty pounds of supplement.

An unexpected benefit of DE was the dramatic reduction in fly problems in the barns and feeding areas. Evidently its desiccant effect destroys the fly larva before it can hatch. Also as the fly picks up the powder on its hairy legs, it is killed as well. Besides being a pest, flies are vectors for disease transmission. The DE also keeps the guard dogs free of ticks and lice.

Another discovery came when we had the misfortune of having to raise a couple of bottle babies. A change in formula, weather stress and overcrowding resulted in coccidiosis. In spite of conventional medical treatment, one died quickly with the other going down hill rapidly, showing no positive response to medication. We had nothing to lose so the second sick kid received two tablespoons of DE with her milk replacer in an eight-ounce bottle. Within 24 hours her rear end was cleaning up, she was eating well and on her way to complete recovery without other toxic treatments to her already compromised immune system. Thereafter we gave her one-teaspoon of dietary grade DE in her bottle daily. Anecdotal evidence, yes, but it would be hard for me to believe that DE did not rescue that very sick kid from certain death.

During one year it cost us roughly $445 to drench 400 adult does with a popular white drench that runs around $79 per 500 ml bottle. A fifty-pound bag of DE sells for about $20 and goes a long way. To the negative rhetoric that diatomaceous earth is not 100% effective at all times, in all circumstances, I say who cares! Every month that I can avoid chemical drenching, I take a proactive stance for staying in business and increasing my bottom line.

For folks who need the assurance of a stamp of approval, please note there is dietary grade diatomaceous earth that is USDA and FDA approved as an anti-caking agent. You probably get it in your cake mixes. It is not going to cut up the insides of your goat as some of the misinformation myths are asserting. DE is a desiccant in addition to being the microscopic skeletal remains of diatoms that scratch the waxy surface of eggs and dries them up. Inside the animal, it causes parasites to release their grip and pass to the outside, but it does not damage mucous membranes. It is used in many organic earthworm farms to control parasites that attack earthworms.

Meanwhile, we are still learning and networking with other goat ranchers who are successfully using DE. Sometimes it's hard to teach old dogs new tricks. I'm sure you'll still see me buy a bottle of conventional drench from time to time but you can bet I'll be watching and trying to learn how to use DE more effectively. I'm learning I can spend more time sitting in my mineral feeder watching my goats and less time resuscitating them from parasite infestation. This Saturday there will be no mad rush to gather goats and vet supplies and do the goaty two step until our muscles ache and our feet throb. We won't be compelled to work goats because of parasites. Instead, I've got time to sit and be bemused by the four-legged critters. Sitting in a mineral feeder may not be your cup of tea, but it's a nice change of pace for me.

New Zealand Import and Herd Sire:
MoneyMaker

Electric fence netting helps to make a quick and easy
pasture addition among the spring plum blossoms.

CHAPTER SIXTEEN

Buying and Selling Goats by The Golden Rule

I imagine most of us were raised by loving parents spouting a handful of favorite truisms. Mom had a lot of favorite sayings. When my sister and I would get to scrappin', Mom would remind us of the Golden rule to "do unto others as we would have others do unto us." We heard it pretty often and it left its mark.

Over the years, we've learned a few things from dealing with breeders of purebred cattle and goats as well as from selling breeding stock ourselves. First and foremost we've learned that we would all have a good start, and it'd be a nicer world, if everyone followed The Golden Rule. We've bought and sold a lot of animals, and we've learned a lot. Tough lessons in the buyer's market can also make you more aware of a better way to buy or sell an animal. Along with following Mama's advice, here are some things we've learned along the way about selling livestock:

Research Your Market

For your sake and your buyer's sake, research your competition and set your prices realistically. Once you make your decision in pricing, stay committed through some reasonable period to time. Selling a few over-priced animals to unsuspecting newcomers and then slashing your asking price for equivalent stock for sales to savvy buyers is not the way to build a good reputation or generate repeat buyers. Avoiding wild fluctuations in your pricing will also prevent the word from getting around that you'll always come down on your prices.

In a free market, supply and demand will pretty much regulate asking and selling price. Nevertheless, as a matter of good business, you need to be sure that you are selling at a price that allows you to recover your costs and see some profit. In order to do that, you'll need to be aware of your cost to raise the animal that you are selling. If the price that you need is not close to the price the market will bear, then some adjustments will need to be made in some area. Perhaps you need to consider a low input management program. Or perhaps you have an unrealistic expectation as to how quickly you can recover your capital investment.

Advertise

The experts tell us that every dollar spent in advertising is a dollar well spent. Of course, times being what they are, we many find ourselves wondering where in our budget does this advertising dollar lie? First, decide how much total outlay in dollars you can afford. Then remember repetition and consistency.

It is better to place a small ad every month than one big one per year with nothing the rest of the time. Even a small classified ad every month or a breeder's listing speaks to your commitment. There are usually price breaks for yearly contracts that are more attractive than advertising on a month to month basis.

Only Sell Your Best as Breeding Stock

Don't sell your problems or culls to other breeders or inexperienced newcomers. They have come to you to avoid the pitfalls of the sale barn and to get something better by buying superior stock. Bad bags, stunted orphans, skinny butted bucks, infertile does and the like should be culled to the sale barn, purebred or not, for slaughter or "buyer beware." Sell only those animals that you would keep and use yourself. This approach will give you the satisfaction of providing a service beyond the sale as you help a fellow farmer or rancher meet their goals.

Private treaty sales earn a premium price reputation by selling premium animals. There's no room for five and dime "loss leaders." If you've had a learning experience with results that are less than what you hoped for, don't advertise these poor quality animals at a low price in hopes of luring buyers for your high priced stuff. Equally unconscionable would be to capitalize on the lack of experience in a new goat rancher. Remember that even purebreds must be culled. As that old time saying goes, "don't be barn blind" – everything in your little red barn is not the best of the breed. If you let greed get in your way of developing the best genetics possible, you will lose sales, and your reputation for having quality stock will decline.

A high-dollar purebred that does not display the best traits the breed has to offer does a disservice to your buyer, your chosen breed association and your future sales. There are occasionally runts or less appealing animals that result from the stacking of recessive genes, management mistakes, injury or illness. Don't buy the line that it doesn't matter what the animal looks like because "the genetics are there." How the animal looks does matter. It may be that the runt's phenotype (the physical characteristics which he displays) accurately reflects his genotype (his genetic makeup that he will pass on). Form follows function and like begets like.

If your purebred is not making a good appearance due to phenotype, illness or injury, then you probably don't want to offer him to a prospective buyer, no matter how great a pedigree he boats. If you are interested in promoting your breed and developing a good reputation, you'll avoid trying to make a quick buck (excuse the pun) by passing off an inferior animal of "good breeding".

Whenever possible, show your buyer the parents of your animal. This may be the best chance to demonstrate full disclosure. There are always exceptions, but most offspring will resemble the parents. This can serve as a good selling tool to show how you expect the youngster to grow out. If you are buying a doe, look at her parents. Ask if she was a twin or triplet. Fertility is heritable. If the doe's dam has a poor udder, don't expect her daughter to be different.

If your buyer has paid a premium for quality breeding stock, he deserves an animal ready to work. Make sure that the animal goes to his new home with a good start including deworming and vaccinations that are up to date.

Accept the fact that raising livestock is not like collecting gold coins. Everyone is not a keeper. You will lose some animals. Some will die and some will disappoint you with their performance. The ones that disappoint you need to be consigned to the local auction barn and not to your customer's high hopes.

Appreciate Your Buyer

Be available to answer questions, supply resource material and refer your buyer to other breeders. Your buyer will appreciate the help. This interchange may lay the foundation for a lasting relationship.

If you are new to farming and ranching and raising goats, don't assume everyone else is new to agriculture as well. People with a long history of farming and ranching have a lot of experience that will transfer positively to goats even if they've never seen one!

Ask your buyer about himself. Find out what his previous experiences include. If he has not raised goats, he will undoubtedly like to hear about your experiences. Perhaps your buyer's experience includes other similar livestock like cattle, also a ruminant. If so, there will be some common ground on which to relate. Remember that it pays to be a good listener.

Some breeders like to give out caps or mugs with their farm name on it or other tokens of their appreciation for the purchase of their livestock. Sometimes a small expenditure can create a lot of goodwill and in turn be good advertising.

Keep Your Paper Work Straight

One of the most common complaints that I've heard regarding registration certificates is that the seller is lax in getting the certificate to the new buyer. Sometimes it's not his fault and the delay lies with the registry but most often, it's the other way around. If someone can take the time to come to your place, view your stock and write you a check, then you should probably find the time to fill out the papers, write a check for the transfer fee and send it off to your registry in a timely manner.

If you are selling registered stock, don't hand your buyer the registration forms and expect him to pay the nominal transfer fees. Whether you've sold a $200 goat or a $2,000 goat, you should expect to pay the transfer fees. Ask your new buyer how he wants his name styled on the registration papers and where you can mail or deliver the papers when they come back from the registry. Obtaining the proper address will help you build a mailing list of your customers. If your customer lives in your area, delivering the papers in person will allow you to follow-up on the status of the animal you sold.

Guarantee Your Livestock

There are no absolutes in biology. Occasionally an animal disappoints us in spite of proper breeding and care. If the animal proves to be a non-breeder or does not perform adequately, you may wish to refund the buyer. It might be hard for some of us to come up with a cash refund when we are selling to make a living, but a seller can stand behind his breeding stock with a breeder's guarantee. This is generally a replacement animal of equal or greater value.

Remember to treat your buyers the same way you would like to be treated. Every sale is an opportunity to make a new friend. Standing behind your sale is an opportunity to keep a friend. A breeder who refuses to do this won't be in the business long although it may seem like an eternity to those whom he has wronged.

Honesty And Integrity At All Times

I've asked other breeders, whom I consider to be exemplary in their dealings, what things are most important in selling breeding stock. All of them agree that honesty and integrity are at the top of the list. If those traits are present, it seems everything else just fall into line.

Verbal contracts may be difficult to litigate in a court of law but in the arena of breeder ethics, your word should be your bond. For example, if you tell a prospective buyer that you will hold an animal for him, perhaps a kid still on its mother, don't sell it to someone else without giving him the chance to obtain – first right of refusal. If you do, you'll lose some credibility, and chances are the buyer will not be happy with a replacement since he'll believe the best one got away. Obtaining a deposit might be the best for both buyer and seller.

It's often said that the world is full of two types of people, givers and takers. A good test for being fair in your dealings would be to ask yourself how you would feel about the trade if you were the buyer instead of the seller. The attitude "Buyer beware" has no place in selling quality breeding stock off the farm. It should remain at the sale barn.

If you tend to be more of a giver in the scheme of give and take, you may find that sometimes your generous nature leaves you with the short end of the stick. In evaluating the fairness of a business deal, when you are the buyer, it might help to pretend you are the seller in that instance. Would you handle the sale in the same manner and feel you have been equitable in your dealings? We all have a sixth sense we can access if we'll pay attention. Some call it a gut feeling or intuition. It helps to listen to those messages you give yourself.

If you've done your work properly, offered your best stock with a breeder's guarantee, answered questions honestly and priced your animals competitively, then you'll make a sale and probably a friend as well. Offering the names and numbers of other breeders in the area will give your buyer the opportunity to buy outcross bloodlines from the ones that you have sold him. It also shows that you are not afraid to have your goats compared with the rest of the breed.

Your breeding program may not have the same goals as another farm's breeding program. Even if you don't agree with another breeder's selection criteria, management practices or personal philosophy, you can still inform your buyer of the available options without negative comments. One of my favorite sayings is "what goes around, comes around". Breeders who are not an asset usually don't last long. At one time it was determined that most purebred breeders only last about five years before they quit. They either become disenchanted with the breed that they are raising or they alienate the agricultural community with whom they network. Unfortunately, some of the worst scoundrels seem to last forever.

If you are thinking about buying or selling breeding stock, remember The Golden Rule and some of the things that are really important in life like fairness, honesty, integrity and being able to look at yourself in the mirror each morning. It's been our experience that most goat ranchers selling breeding stock are fine people and I would not want to suggest that buying goats makes one vulnerable to plunder and pillage, nor would I suggest that there are many buyers or sellers who might not follow The Golden Rule. After all, goat ranchers are a great group of people!

CHAPTER SEVENTEEN

Don't Lose Heart

A bout the time we made a big commitment to raise meat goats it seemed as if the new goat industry was exploding. Newcomers joined the ranks daily and all of us looked for more advice on how to raise goats profitably. Fortunately the thrust of the novice's enthusiasm will generally help him over the bumpy spots in the learning curve. Sometimes the first year is the roughest and sometimes not. Sometimes it gets worse in the days to follow as we reap the results of our inexperience. Sometimes it becomes a challenge to not lose heart.

Several years ago I read a book by Hallie Crawford Stillwell entitled *I'll Gather My Geese* published by Texas A & M University Press. It was historical and entertaining but it was also a study in the continual challenge to succeed in any agricultural venture. In this case it was ranching beef cattle on the open range of South Texas after the turn of the century. Hallie was one of the first women ranchers, city bred like myself, she married Roy Stillwell and moved to the Stillwell Ranch in 1918. She worked alongside her husband, fighting the daily challenges of weather, livestock, facilities and the market. Late in life her husband was killed in an accident. It could be said that it was his time when she was left alone to carry on. However, the overriding impression I carried away from the story was that it was his time because he had lost heart.

There are many newcomers to goat ranching looking around and asking themselves if this is an enterprise at which they can succeed. I think we have to realize the answer is "yes" but we must not lose heart as we continue along the learning curve. We must also realize that we each live in a unique situation. Our animals, our ecological environment and our capital resources are all different. We must find a balance that works to our satisfaction in our situation. Most of us need to realize a satisfactory profit in order to continue. Therefore, cost efficient production is the goal. For others, raising goats may fall into the pet category where social interaction, both with the goat and prospective buyer, is the main concern and no one counts the number of feed bags hauled home each month. For those of us who are trying to make a living, rather than pursue a social activity, we need to earn financial rewards in order not to lose heart.

When cost efficient production is the goal, we must learn what choices to make to bring us to that point. We must choose the best goat for our operation. There are many good goats and the differences within breeds can be as great and as diverse as it is between breeds. We need to remember to put a priority on those traits that will best suit our environment. If we have plenty of cash or abundant food sources, full-time hired help and a lack of predators, then the traits we choose can be those which will produce the prettiest, heaviest goat possible. If our environment is hostile and our food sources marginal, then we need a hardy, hustling, surviving goat. Despite the breeder hype we see in advertisements claiming to have the ultimate goat, you can't have your cake and eat it too, as Mom used to say.

Some traits are inversely related. In other words, you give up or diminish one in order to increase or obtain the other. Heavy, double muscling does not equate to easy birthing. The only goat kids we pulled from our first-time Spanish does were the heavier muscled, big boned types. A high loss due to dystocia does not contribute to cost efficient production. Our personal experience with a couple of popular breeds of goats has shown us that those pretty, big boned kids sometimes have bigger, harder to deliver heads, shoulders and hips. Kids that arrive bruised and exhausted from a difficult birth are slower to rise and seek the udder. Excessively fat or heavily muscled dams can be the lazy kidders we hear more about since the arrival of some of the heavier new meat goat breeds.

In cattle, heavy muscling is inversely proportional to heavy milking as well. Heavy muscled cows, more often than not, will not milk as heavily as their thinner counterpart. The Holstein or Jersey milk cow with her bony hip area is the perfect example. It is important for us to stress strong maternal traits in our dams. We need good mothers in our goat herd with plentiful milk. If we are keeping replacement does, then we should select a balanced sire that will complement the dam's strengths by siring a vigorous, fast growing kid while maintaining strong maternal traits. If we are selling all our kids, then we can select a terminal sire that will produce heavy, fast growing kids. We need to remember our best economic goal is to produce a kid of desirable market weight at weaning.

Often the photos of barrel fat goats are similar to photos of Sumo wrestlers whom we would not consider average or even superior in human stature. They are just overfed. As Dr. Frank Pinkerton, retired goat specialist, says, "A fat goat is not a healthy goat." Experience teaches us to recognize excessive inputs that create the illusion of a superior goat. But, there is only one way to develop that experience and that is to get out there and do it. And within the boundaries of our individual farms, we can select from those goat families that do the best job for our replacement stock.

But genetics are only part of the equation. Perhaps even more important is the forage we have to offer our critters. Unless we are raising pets in pens, we are primarily grass farmers. The goats are our harvesting machinery and we must learn to use them in an efficient manner to harvest the grass, forbs and browse grown by the free sunlight. We have a free source of energy supplied by the sun and we have a renewable resource in the green growing stuff. Our job is to supply the fencing, and learn about stocking rates and intensively managed rotational grazing.

The most dramatic phenomenon to newcomers of rotational grazing is the increase in plant species that results. As plant diversity increases, livestock health seems to improve as a result of the smorgasbord of micronutrients being accessed by the different plants. Additional benefits of intensive grazing include drought protection. Paddocks are rested and the grass becomes thick and lush. When the rains don't come, there is a protective cover holding the moisture in and allowing the grass to continue to grow unlike the areas that are continually grazed and eaten down to bare dirt.

Goat ranching in unlikely parts of the country is an additional challenge to new goat ranchers facing less brittle environments than the ones goats have traditionally been raised in. Higher parasite exposure and lower levels of microminerals in the forages are two important tradeoffs to the more abundant forage. There will be even more issues to resolve and problems to solve than just being new to goats.

It takes time to learn to do something well. When we learned to walk we fell down a lot. Some of those falls might have included hitting our head on a coffee table or stair step. Some falls were just more painful than others were but none of them kept us from getting up and trying again. Learning new things includes failures and we need to remember that those people who have succeeded at great things were most often the same people who experienced miserable failures along the way.

If we choose to play it safe and only do those things that we already know how to do, then we shut the door to the opportunity to learn how to do something else well also. We seldom learn anything startling when we repeat the same old thing but we learn a lot from our failures. The critical difference is what we do with the new information. We can throw in the towel or we can pick ourselves up and do it better the second time around. The human condition requires purpose and challenge. Goat ranching can certainly provide both if we just don't lose heart.

PART FOUR

About Our Anatolians

(left)
Two and a half year old D'Artagnan greets his owner.

(below)
A four and a half month old Anatolian male displays good guarding behavior with his alert response to unfamiliar sound or movement in the brush.

CHAPTER EIGHTEEN

Anatolian Shepherd Livestock Guardian Dogs

Today's Anatolian Shepherd Livestock Guardian Dog can trace its roots back 6,000 years to ancient times when nomadic tribes wandered between the area now called Tibet and Denmark, later settling on the Anatolian Plains of Turkey. As a member of a tight group, where life was characterized by danger, uncertainty, and constant travel in search of grazing lands, the Anatolian Shepherd was heavily selected for the traits that have made it famous.

When a new litter was born, only the best pup was kept, the others were destroyed. Survival required every member to contribute. The dogs earned their keep by preserving and protecting not only the flock but the shepherd as well. Mountain lions and bears were no match for the lithe and powerful Anatolian. A stranger on horseback would think twice before entering an encampment where the sentry was "coban kopek", a Turkish expression meaning shepherd's dog.

Yet, as intimidating and regal an image as the Anatolian on guard projects, he is a loving and devoted member of his human family. Easily socialized to people, the Anatolian guardian dog will interface with the human family while defending his charges with his life, if necessary. An Sheps, as they are affectionately called by some owners, are typical of livestock guardian dogs in that they guard from a defensive position. They are not attack dogs or herding dogs. They use their deep bark and high profile to warn predators away. If necessary, they will engage them. Usually their presence is enough to drive away potential marauders who would plunder and terrorize a shepherd's flock.

The Anatolian Shepherd pups begin their bonding with the stock they will eventually guard at a young age. At Caston Creek Ranch in the Ouchita Mountain Range of Southeastern Oklahoma, Anatolian Shepherd pups are whelped and raised in the pasture and timber with the goat herd. When they open their eyes and begin to wobble out to explore the world, they are likely to see baby goats. It is not unusual to see these dogs exhibiting mature guarding behavior as early as four months although full emotional maturity will come later, usually by the age of eighteen months. Early bonding helps the pups to identify their responsibility and feel at home with the herd. However, the guarding behavior is so deeply imbedded in the DNA that even dogs raised with people, and later taken to farms, have been known to instinctively guard the livestock.

The size range for the Anatolian Shepherd runs from about 27 to 36 inches in height and 120 to 180 pounds. Males, of course, are larger than females. Their lithe structure, almost greyhound in appearance, allows them to leap, lunge and twist in the air to avoid the predator while driving him off. The conformation of the Anatolian resulted from centuries of battling predators and the elements. Some breeders are concerned that the recent acceptance of the Anatolian Shepherd into the AKC will encourage show ring criteria to develop that may be at cross-purposes with their true working heritage.

These dogs are efficient converters and require only a modest amount of food for a large dog. Additionally, they have the ability to tolerate weather extremes from high temperatures over 100° in the summer to severe cold in the winter. There are numerous stories of Anatolian Shepherds who have put the welfare of their livestock before their own comfort.

If it were possible to give an intelligence test to dogs, Anatolian Shepherds may well be the Albert Einsteins of the dog world. They are

*While we were busy talking, Babe was paying attention
and determined to keep Curt out of the pond.*

extremely intelligent. An owner rarely has to repeat himself to make a point to the dogs. Even at a very young age, the Anatolian learns quickly and does not repeat mistakes.

When my first grandson was 15 months old, we bought our first two Anatolians, Tex and Babe. They came to us at the tender age of 4 and one half weeks. We fed them puppy chow with lamb replacer and kept them with some newborn bottle babies. Every day we would walk the quarter mile from the house to the barn and visit the little pups. Curtis was walking pretty well by then and he would walk over and pet the pups or try to pick one up.

Within a few weeks the pups had grown considerably and one day when we visited, one jumped up, put his paws on Curt's chest and knocked him down causing the child to cry. I shook my finger at the pup and sharply told him "Don't you ever jump on that baby!" He never did again, and neither did his litter mate who was watching. We walked to the barn the next day and both pups eagerly greeted Curt and gently licked his ear while waiting to be petted.

Although the guarding behavior is bred into the dog, there needs to be some supervision during early periods and through adolescence. Like teenagers feeling their oats, Babe and Tex tried playing with the goats at least once. We quickly squashed that idea with a firm reprimand. A few weeks later we were heaping praise on Babe for keeping the grandson from wandering into a pond while the adults were busy talking. She turned her body sideways and stubbornly refused to let the child proceed any further toward the water. Always on duty, always guarding all that is dear to the family.

Anatolians also have a reputation of being hardheaded as well as inde-pendent. Undoubtedly these characteristics arise from their sure knowl-edge and confident assessment of their guarding duties. Many a rancher has deferred to his Anatolian's instincts. Patrolling, barking, signaling the livestock when danger is near, are all part of the An Shep's repertoire.

In rough country, ranchers will frequently run two or more guardian dogs. When the dogs are alerted to danger, they will signal the herd of goats, which in turn will bunch up into a tight group. The signals they use to communicate with their charges range from a quick bark to alert them to danger to the use of body language, turning sideways and curl-ing their long full tails. One dog will stay with the herd and the other will approach the danger, barking a warning for the intruder to retreat.

Anatolian Shepherd guardian dogs are even known to help with the birthing process. Many dogs have helped a doe clean up her newly kid-ded offspring, then retreated to watch the new family bond. A couple of years ago, while walking the pasture looking for chilled newborns, we found one of the male dogs lying next to a wet newborn, sheltering it from the wind while its mother labored to have the second kid. An Anatolian considers such feats all part of a day's work.

Anatolian Shepherd breeders are encouraged to be selective in both breeding their dogs and in selling them. Registries encourage breeders to maintain high standards in breeding and to screen prospective buyers. Buyers need to know that most Anatolian Shepherd breeders are looking at them as closely as they are looking at the new puppies. Breeders often ask questions about the environment into which the newly purchased dog will be arriving. Will there be adequate space to maintain a large working breed? Does the buyer have proper housing and fencing to prevent the dog from becoming a liability? Will a barking dog present a problem to neighbors? Does the buyer have the time necessary to provide proper care? Will the buyer be able to handle a strong willed dog? Will the buyer be willing to neuter or spay working stock to prevent unwanted litters? These and many other questions are important considerations for those who wish to breed dogs to sell.

Prospective purchasers of any dog breed, and especially the independent An Shep, are well advised to think long and hard on the obligation they assume when bringing a dog into their family or working environment. Time spent reading about the traits of these animals is time well spent. Be especially aware of the information and resources available on-line for your breed. In a recent Internet search, I found a site for the National Anatolian Shepherd Rescue Network. They listed reasons why dogs end up in a rescue situation. Many failures could be avoided by thorough pre-purchase research including visiting with breeders and other owners.

There are several different clubs and views vary among the members. Some owners show their dogs and have them registered in two or more registries including AKC. Others, mostly working ranches, abhor the idea of a noble Anatolian trotting around on a leash. They see their dignity and purpose compromised by emphasizing show ring conformation that may not coincide with the function for which they were bred. Form should follow function not the judge's whims.

Livestock guardian dogs require commitment from their owners to provide them with adequate health care, nutrition and most importantly, the opportunity for a life of service. They ask for little more than to be allowed to do that for which they were bred – to serve as a faithful guardian to their assigned charges. So few enterprises in life are as rewarding as owning a working Anatolian Shepherd Guardian Dog.

Grandson Curtis visits Babe's new pups.

A new kid is cleaned up by his mom while a Round Bottom Ranch An Shep provides shelter in the snow.
(Photo by Gene Blackwell)

CHAPTER NINETEEN

A Rite of Passage

When Babe and Tex were only six months old, we found ourselves about to face a wreck with the post bottle babies. It was all part of the learning curve. We learned we didn't like raising bottle babies and we learned that confining them was the recipe for disaster. We came home from our off farm job to find the group we called the "weaners" in trouble. Thirty-two weaners had been penned in a 100-by-40 foot horse wire enclosure with free choice feed and anytime access to a half acre of bermuda grass topped off with a newly baled roll of hay.

The small area combined with a wetter than normal summer was the perfect recipe for disaster. We ran beyond the recommended 21 to 28 day worming schedule by about 10 days and we had not yet learned about fresh water dietary grade DE. We lost one doe before we even had a diagnosis of the problem. We quickly treated the does with injectable Ivomec but lost another before the sun set. Thirty-six hours after treatment, the edema subsided and we appeared to be moving in a positive direction.

Our two Anatolian pups, Tex and Babe were six months old and 80 pounds each. They had joined the little nannies to become their friends and guardians when they were only four and one-half weeks of age. We had kept both the does and the puppies penned for fear that at such tender ages they would all be coyote bait. The next thing we knew we were faced with a dilemma. We could see that the group of commercial crossbred goats left to forage a larger area was not having the same parasite problem. Still, we were not sure we could move two six month old puppies and their little doelings to another, less secure pasture.

A small four acre grass trap near the house was occupied by a small group of weaned heifers that had some trouble keeping up with the grass and pigweed. It seemed like the only alternative to the infested pen. However, we worried that if we moved the weaners and the pups into it, Tex and Babe might be tempted to leave the goats to join Fritz, the farm dog. Or perhaps, they might take to wandering or chasing the heifers; not to mention what might happen if a pack of coyotes came onto the scene.

A full-grown Anatolian male might weigh as much as 160 pounds and easily handle a few coyotes or a bobcat, but these pups were still babies. By the first of October the coyotes were brazen. We hadn't even seen a frost much less a hard killing freeze. We could only wonder how much worse it would be later when their food supply diminished. At night we could hear them yelping across the creek from the house, not fifty yards away, in the hay field we call the "Black Cow Meadow". After some discussion, we decided death by parasites was probably worse than by coyotes. We would just have to take some risk and put the doelings into some pasture that had never known goats.

We moved the group, along with their Port-A-Hut, trough and creep feeder into the grass trap we called "the Triangle." Nervously, I started to spend time watching the pups' behavior. Soon I was watching in admiration as Tex and Babe assumed the role they were bred and born to play.

The little does moved through the grass, nibbling the seedheads from the pigweed and tasting other morsels that offered themselves. They moved like a little beehive, staying in close proximity to each other. Tex and Babe maneuvered silently among their charges. Babe walked back and forth as if counting to see if all were present. Sometimes they took turns lying down, as if one was resting while the other patrolled.

Eventually, it happened. A little test for the rookie guard dogs. The curious heifers had made their way over to where the goats were grazing. Tex and Babe moved from the middle of the group and positioned themselves between the heifers and the goats. They sat side by side several yards apart facing the group of bovines with their girls behind them blissfully grazing. The pups looked so serious about their business as they intently watched the heifers that I laughed aloud. The heifers never came any closer and when they changed direction and moved on, Tex and Babe rejoined their does.

Later several heifers came upon the goats' water trough while walking the fence line, as cattle seem to like to do. They didn't realize that Babe was not going to let them put their noses in her goats' water as she quickly ran up and barked them away. They backed up, turned around and walked away, probably wondering what new intrusion was in their pasture. Babe followed them for a short distance just to make sure they were leaving. Babe sat for a minute watching them and when she felt sure they were gone she rejoined her girls.

We were bone tired by the time it got dark that day. Securing a gate that would allow only the goats into the steel paneled corral where the creep feeder was located was the only thing we didn't get accomplished. We brought Babe and Tex their dinner and since the does had the new pasture, we figured they would be fine until morning without the creep feed. It had been a good day and we had seen enough to be fairly certain that we would get a good night's sleep.

Morning came and we awoke to find the goats and the dogs gone. We jumped into the truck and a few minutes later found them all hanging around the barn, near their old pen, wanting that molasses cereal that they had grown to love. Tex and Babe were dutifully guarding their goats. Fortunately, it only took the rattle of a feed bucket to ring them back to the new pasture. I promised myself that by this time next year they would have to make it just on forage.

We rigged the gate on the corral, ran two more strands of barbed wire to goat proof a deficient section of fence, and sat back to survey the scene. The pups were sticking like glue to those little goats. The move to this pasture had been a rite of passage for Tex and Babe. They were only six months old and eighty pounds, but we figured those coyotes probably knew there were two big dogs on Caston Creek who would not be putting up with any shenanigans.

Curt tells Babe that her puppies are heavy.

D'Artagnan shares storytime with Curtis.

CHAPTER TWENTY

We Lost Our Hearts to Anatolians

S ome things in life are planned and you know long before they come about that, God willing, they will happen. After we moved back to the ranch, we knew we wanted to find a way to make a living there so that we could stay. We planned on having cattle to eat the grass. Eventually we hoped to get our fences to the point where we could have goats. Finally, we got the goats. These additions were all part of some long term planning. It required an investment of capital, time and effort accompanied by tears, laughter and lots of sore muscles. We had even planned on a guard dog or two for the goats.

What we didn't plan on was falling in love with some big dog from Turkey. We had never even heard of an Anatolian Shepherd much less seen one. Then one spring day, there we were driving out of the Edward's Plateau with a load of goats and two four and one-half week old balls of fur, muscle and bone. They were our first Anatolian Shepherds. We named them Tex and Babe.

We had owned several farm dogs and hunting dogs and, like most families with pets, we had grown attached to them. But, after all, they were just dogs. Nothing had prepared me for the impact this noble breed of canine, called Anatolian Shepherd, would have on me. Their intelligence and their devotion to their charges have filled me with unending admiration. Our two West Texas dogs have been so extraordinary that we felt we had an obligation to help preserve the working genetics that they displayed by breeding Babe to the very best male we could find.

Sometimes synchronicity sets the stage. When Babe came into heat at Christmas, my attention returned to the idea of breeding her, the following year, to a fine dog. Little did I know that her future sweetheart had been born on Christmas Eve on a sheep and goat farm in Charlottesville, Virginia. Michele Mangham had read about Tex and Babe and our embryo work in an issue of the *Goat Rancher* magazine. She dropped us a note letting us know of her new litter and telling us a little about Mangham Manor Mohair. We followed up a month later with a phone call and received a video showing the new litter. They were seven little Sherman Tanks, one of the most uniform looking set of puppies that I've sever seen. They were all equally beautiful; nevertheless, we did pick one of the bigger males who appeared, perhaps, a little more alert in the video. Michele was also very helpful in guiding us toward a decision.

Since this was Michele's "D" litter, she asked that we pick a name starting with "D". We settled on D'Artagnan, the leader of the three musketeers. D'Artagnan was a valiant soldier and a dashing figure to the ladies. We would call the puppy "Dar" for short and he would be the great defender of Caston Creek as well as Babe's knight in shining armor.

Dar flew into DFW on Delta Dash, counter to counter service for a total airfare of $153.00. He weighed roughly twenty pounds at eight weeks and flew in his little dog carrier from Charlottesville to Dallas via Cincinnati. After about six hours in the air, he may have been quite certain that the world as he knew it was over.

Michele had gone out to the pasture early that morning to retrieve the pup for the flight. For the first time he was severed from his siblings and his protest was the last thing Michele heard from him as husband Joel drove away to the airport.

Papa took the fawn colored pup out of the carrier and put him in my lap. He buried his dark nose in the folds in my coat and lay silently for some time. Soon he relaxed and lifted his head to survey his surroundings. Four hours later we arrived at the ranch. Dar had recovered from any flight trauma and was ready to explore. We walked down a ranch road and met two year old Curtis who announced "Nana bring me puppy." Curtis and Dar made their acquaintance and I was impressed with the calm nature of this little critter.

It was getting late so I walked Dar down to the goats to meet Tex and Babe. The big dogs acted like they were going to eat Dar. I decided we were both too tired and would fight that battle another day. Besides, the weather was cold and dreary. We welcomed Dar into the kitchen to enjoy his dinner. Lara and Curtis sat around on the kitchen floor watching him. He ate well, looked around briefly and then climbed happily into Lara's lap. Michele's words, "Now don't spoil him," came rushing back to me as Dar looked entirely too comfortable imitating a lap dog.

We moved Dar to a penned area of the adjoining deck where he spent the night alternating between crying and sleeping. Morning came but before we could make the trip back to Tex, Babe and the goats, it started to pour. We knew we could not leave the puppy in the house all day playing with the inhabitants and then expect him to joyfully return to the pasture so we put him in the cattle trailer with a newly orphaned calf. Dar whined a little and we thought "well, at least he'll be happy to see the goats when the weather clears."

By morning he was best buddies with the calf and when I called him out of the trailer he bounced back to the calf and looked at me as if to say "can I keep him, Mom?" Certainly that attitude attests to the Anatolian's resilience and adaptability. In less than twenty-four hours, he had become a calf guard dog.

Finally we took Dar down to the recip pen (without his calf) and Tex and Babe came up to check him out. Babe still behaved as if she wanted to annihilate the small pup. We scolded the big dogs with mixed feelings since we do want them to remain hostile to coyotes, bobcats and strange dogs. Tex settled down immediately next to the horse wire where Dar was hiding on the other side between the water trough and the fence. Babe continued to act menacing. After some discussion, we put Tex in with Dar. Dar was euphoric to be with another dog! Tex lay down and Dar jumped all over him. Tex was unflappable. Babe stopped barking when we put Tex in with the small pup. She looked more disgusted than confused by Tex's obvious tolerance.

Tex and Dar are inseparable in the recipient paddock. We expected Tex to show his new apprentice the ropes and he did. Whenever Tex was alerted by something strange and ran barking to see what it was, Dar was right behind him. During the day Dar could be found lying in the hay with his new family of recipient nannies and embryo kids. He knew he'd found a home on Caston Creek.

In time Dar became a mature dog and Babe came into season. Before we knew it, we had our own litter of little Sherman Tanks following the goats around the banks of Caston Creek. We wondered how we had managed to live all these years without an Anatolian in our family and in our hearts.

CHAPTER TWENTY-ONE

No News is Good News

One year when Terry Hankins, editor of the Goat Rancher Magazine, asked me to share my perspective on Guard Dogs for the December edition of Goat Rancher Magazine, my initial reaction was that there was nothing to tell—no exciting stories of life and death on Caston Creek! Terry reminded me that maybe nothing happening was the story. Sometimes no news is good news.

Nothing was happening because there were four big dogs that made their presence known to marauding bands of menacing four-legged trespassers who might long for a succulent snack of goat. Perspective is everything. A few decades ago I would have been an irate city dweller if I awoke to the deep, repeating sounds of several big dogs barking in unison. Now I sleep like a baby knowing my dogs have everything safely under control.

The dogs were our four Anatolian Shepherds, Tex, Babe, D'Artagnon and Blaze. Tex and Babe came from Marble Falls in West Texas. D'Artagnon flew from Charlottesville, Virginia where he left the pastures at a very tender age. Blaze, a brindle colored female, was out of a dam that traveled in utero from Turkey. There just wasn't much going on.

Tex was feeling a little humiliated in those days because we moved him in with a temporarily boarded Great Pyrenees pup named "Lebo". Tex did his job, making sure the puppy didn't let the natural exuberance of youth overstep the bounds of propriety in goat play and safety. Together they guarded a group of weanlings. Before that Tex had begun enjoying lying around the yard a bit too much after spending summer days guarding (he thought) our daughter, Amanda, as she painted the house exterior for us. Mandy had a soft spot in her heart for Tex. Tex sensed that and repaid her affection with loyalty but those lazy summer days were over and now he had a juvenile to rear and a group of weaned kids to protect.

During that time D'Artagnon and the two females were left as constant companions with the main herd out along Caston Creek. The main herd was mostly commercial goats, squired around by our New Zealand Import "MoneyMaker". There are also several registered does running with the commercial mob. The fact that we let our valuable imported buck roam free to enjoy the winter forbs and grasses, rather than safely penning him, spoke to our faith and confidence in the dogs.

We live in the heart of coyote and big cat country, with purported sightings of black bears. I awake with a start when a pack of coyotes make the rounds and start to howl close in to the house. Before my head lifts far from the pillow, the deep baying warnings from our faithful guardians lull me back to sleep.

I've never seen such commitment as I see daily in our Anatolian Shepherds. We were late feeding the dogs one evening. Usually we would try to feed them before it got too late in the day but time got away from us and it was after dark. We drove to the spot where we had been accustomed to meeting the trio and filling their bowls. Only the two females appeared. I called D'Artagnon repeatedly, knowing the main herd was settling down for the night about one quarter mile away in a wooded grove down along the creek bank. I also knew Dar could easily hear me calling him to dinner. When he didn't come we drove back in the dark to where we had last seen the goats congregating.

There was Dar, lying in the middle of the goats, waiting for Babe and Blaze to return so that he could leave to eat his dinner. Dar, a huge dog already, wouldn't be a year old until Christmas Eve but that didn't stop him from taking his responsibilities seriously. Although he knew it was safe to stray short distances from the herd in broad daylight, he was undoubtedly certain that the goats needed him close when darkness fell. The safety of his charges came before the gnawing in his stomach. It would not have mattered how long I called that dog to dinner. Nothing can deter a hardheaded Anatolian from his duty.

Slowly these dogs have taught me how they work and, despite my occasional frustration, they usually know best. The dog food bill at the ranch runs pretty high these days but we think it is still a bargain at twice the price.

(above)
Angel watching over her does as they graze along the banks of Caston Creek.

(below)
Anatolian Guardian Dog on patrol at Round Bottom Ranch.
(Photo by Gene Blackwell)

CHAPTER TWENTY-TWO

Angel –
the Guardian Angel

I ndian summer days, warm sun on my face and the prospect of another Thanksgiving Turkeyfest on Caston Creek always gave me a reason to count my blessings. After a year like 1998, drought and pestilence adding its toll to the bottomed out cattle cycle, it was uplifting to be urged to think about the gifts we receive in spite of hard times. Sometimes life's gifts come at unexpected moments in unexpected ways.

Years of breeding cattle and nearly a decade with a closed herd found us liquidating ruthlessly, again. Armyworms invaded, devoured the winter pasture and closed down any chance to recover before winter. The gift was the goats. They became our central "ag" endeavor and showed us how they could utilize even the most forsaken forage in the poorer, timbered areas. They presented a flexibility we didn't have with cattle.

The turn of events that year in agriculture made off farm jobs even more critical to many small family farms. Ours was no exception. However, long distance ranching, even with the best of hired help, presents some problems. We had an early June litter of Anatolian Shepherd pups. We wanted all of our growing dogs to be closely supervised to insure that they had every opportunity to develop the traits for which they were born and bred.

Since we couldn't be home every day, we made arrangements with our good friends at Round Bottom Ranch near Heavener, Oklahoma. Gene Blackwell, goat breeder and experienced hand at assessing and working with livestock guardian dogs, came to our aid. So off the pups went to LGD training camp. When we checked in with Gene, he always had a bright story for us about their progress.

Gene lives in a lush bottom, surrounded by hundred of acres of timber and all the resident predators. His goats overnight near the barns but in the morning they head for the timber with the dogs in tow. Dutifully the pups in training went along. In the beginning, when they were somewhat younger and inexperienced, one or two of the youngsters might return to the barn during the afternoon. But soon they all stayed out all day, coming in only before dark to overnight with the goatherd.

One evening when the group returned from the timber, Gene noticed that one of the pups was missing along with one of his mature Great Pyrenees dogs. Gene looked for the dogs but darkness fell before he could find them and he knew he would have to wait until morning. At dawn he found his Great Pyrenees female on a pond bank where she had a vantage point. One more time she pointed Gene to the absent creatures, as she often did when livestock were found missing. The missing pup, a little brindle female, lay bedded down next to a goat who had spent the night with her head caught in a piece of old fence. The young dog had undoubtedly become that doe's guardian angel for the night.

Our Anatolian Shepherds were always inspiring awe and reinforcing our faith in them with such acts of dedication. And for a four and one-half month old pup, I'd have to say she showed a great deal of courage. It's got to be pretty scary staying out in the dark alone without the security of the group and the other dogs. Maybe the Great Pyrenees matron knew this little dog needed that rite of passage and so she watched her from afar. We decided to keep the little An Shep pup and name her "Angel". We think Angel is one of life's gifts to us.

Angel made it back home in time for Thanksgiving and received her very own group of Caston Creek does. The grandkids loved Angel and would insist on letting her into the yard when they could lure her away from her goats. They would pet her, hug her, and feed her scraps but still she remained always ready to go back to the goats. Papa and I enjoyed watching our most precious gifts play with Angel and we knew that life had blessed us in the very best of ways.

(left)
No matter where these does venture, they are closely watched over by a faithful Anatolian.
(Photo by Gene Blackwell)

(below)
Tex keeps an eye open for danger in the midst of the goat herd.

CHAPTER TWENTY-THREE

Missing Tex

We'll remember the drought that came to Caston Creek in the summer of 1998 for a long time. For most Americans, the drought meant five minutes of the 6:00 o'clock news devoted to stories of scorched crops and pastures, dried up water tanks, sacrificed livestock and falling prices. For the farmers and ranchers who lived it, there was rarely five minutes of relief. The effect and subsequent losses suffered were far-reaching. Beyond the losses of the pocket book, there were losses that tried the soul of many.

We were luckier than most ranchers in some ways. We had dispersed most of the cattle in anticipation of the coming drought. The goats took to the timber and managed to find a meal there until late summer when they started venturing onto the neighbors on the north and the south. The neighbor on the north welcomed the goats. He had personal experience that showed him how goats could improve his pasture for his cows by clearing brush and making more grass. The neighbor on the south also said he had no problem with the goats. We assumed that meant that he too knew what a benefit the goats could be as environmentally friendly herbicides.

Although we preferred that our livestock stay at home, we believed that since both neighbors seemed to welcome them, we could offer their brush clearing, herbicidal activity in exchange for the additional forage. After all, we all know that in some areas of the country people pay good money to have goat herds brought in to reduce fuel loads or clear brush. Both neighbors were aware that three or four guardian dogs traveled with the herd at all times.

Sometime during their travels south, apparently bored grown children chased the goats on four-wheelers. When this happened, our faithful guardian dogs would bark and run along side the four-wheelers, undoubtedly trying to stop the motored monsters from attacking their charges. Two and one-half year old Tex was often at the forefront holding off the attackers with his barking while Babe and D'Artagnan took the herd to safety. At least once he was not quick enough and a young kid was found dead with tire tracks across its body. Four-wheelers can be a more difficult challenge than a hungry mountain lion.

So when the big truck came into the pasture toward the goats, Tex knew he should bark it back before it hurt another unsuspecting doe or kid. He ran along side it barking. It stopped and a man got out. Tex stopped and looked at the man. The man looked at Tex and shot him dead.

When Papa called the neighbor who had no problem with the goats, he asked him if Tex had threatened him, barred his teeth or growled. The man said no. The dog had merely been running along side the truck. But the man was afraid of dogs; especially big dogs so he shot the gentle guardian because of an irrational fear of some imagined incident that would never have happened.

We didn't know that the neighbor on the south was afraid of dogs or that he didn't understand the difference between a livestock guardian dog and a trained attack dog. Maybe somewhere he heard about attack guard dogs that can take a man down and even kill him. But guardian dogs defend, not attack. Our dogs are socialized to people and children since birth and when the man got out of the truck, Tex probably thought he had come to help him protect the herd from the menacing wheels that kept trying to get his goats. In my mind I can see big gentle Tex standing there waiting for the man to come over and lay his hand on top of his big broad head and say, "good boy, Tex, you stopped those big wheels from getting your goats."

Fear and ignorance are hard to combat. Maybe we could have done some things differently. We ran a mile of field fencing up against the existing barbed wire fence to try to keep them on the place, but goats are fierce foragers and the drought was especially bad. In retrospect, I wish we had invited our neighbor over and called the dogs up so he could see how gentle they are with people and especially small children. Maybe we could have told them how their guarding behavior has been bred into them over centuries, going back to the guarding of flocks and nomadic tribes on the Anatolian Plains of Turkey. Maybe if he had understood, he would have seen that the drivers of the four-wheelers were just a little bored with life and trying to stir up some excitement by pushing his fear buttons. Maybe he would have seen that the dogs were only trying to stand between the perceived threat and the herd, defending not attacking, with their deep bark and impressive size. Instead, he killed a valuable dog.

In M. Scott Peck's book "Denial of the Soul", he says that the man's irrational fear and phobia "displaces his existential fear, which he is unwilling to face, onto a seemingly more manageable object. The essence is the fear of death and dying. Most phobias are traceable to this basic existential fear."

Reason rarely triumphs over rampant fear. It is unlikely that we can help our neighbor face his most basic fear but maybe we could have done more to thwart this tragedy.

I don't know what happens to guardian dogs when their time comes, but I think our Maker probably has provided a place for them. A creature with such intelligence, loyalty and spirit surely cannot be lost to eternity. We knew that in time we would overcome the pain just as we would recover from the effects of the drought. We've reinforced more fence line but we're still missing Tex.

Darby and Jo

Jewel and Dar

CHAPTER TWENTY-FOUR

Zorro Saves the Day

Agoat producer who employs Anatolian Shepherds to guard his stock will find that his or her life is filled with one heartwarming story after another. At least that has been our experience. One of our eight-month-old working dogs, named Zorro, was guarding a group of goats in a rough timbered area. The weather was unusually turbulent and we guessed it was part of the La Nina early spring that we were having.

One day Zorro tangled with something *very bad*. He limped back to the temporary facility with punctures in his throat, neck and front leg, and marks on his rear. Thirty-seven registered goats were missing. The older dogs had come in with another group and although they may have come to his rescue, we could not tell. It was possible that the strong winds, dense trees, hills and ravines would mask the sound of the commotion so that they did not hear him.

We whisked the pup to the vet. The swelling and bruising was quite bad and he was in some pain. Zorro never growled or complained at any of us, including the vet handling him. Our canine specialist in the nearby town of Poteau, Dr. Stokes, commented that he was amazed at the attitude of these Anatolian Shepherds. "They don't have a mean bone in their body," he said. And yet they are ferocious guardians, willing to lay down their life for their charges.

Zorro is only an adolescent, not too long removed from his puppy days. Yet he stood his ground like a mature guardian, fighting to protect his herd. It appeared that his leather collar kept him from receiving more wounds on his neck, so we are wondering if something close to an authentic Turkish collar might be an asset when the dogs are in the war zone.

As we were leaving the clinic, Dr. Stokes said, "He did his job and he's learned some things. He'll be a better fighter next time." That may seem like a paradoxical statement about a most gentle creature, but that's our Anatolians.

We returned home to find all of the goats, including the thirty-seven that we thought were missing, waiting at the facility. Zorro's group had scattered during the battle, returning to the safety net of the other dogs. Zorro stayed at the clinic for a couple of days but now he is back, strong and vigilant, guarding his girls on Caston Creek.

PART FIVE

Essays on Goat Ranching and the Family Farm in America

*A Round Bottom Ranch Guardian stays near
a goat caught in the fence. (Photo by Gene Blackwell)*

These does are busy nipping the early spring browse.

CHAPTER TWENTY-FIVE

Oats and
Fetlocks

W hen I heard Papa muttering about oats and fetlocks, I figured he must have heard about some new nutritional disease or something. I found out pretty quickly that what he was saying was "why would anyone put *goats in feedlots*"! No wonder I thought I had heard something else. It was probably the first time in my half century of walking this planet that I had heard the words "goats and feedlots" in the same breath. It sounded like an incredible oxymoron, but, hey, I'm all for checking out a new idea even one that causes me to gasp a little.

Now it's a well-known fact that until the high dollar imports, brush (meat) goats never commanded an impressive asking price. There was some bragging rights that accompanied the purchase of a two thousand-dollar breeding bull, but the twenty dollar brush goat wasn't worth mentioning. However, meat goats claimed the right to live peacefully amid more venerated livestock because they just didn't cost much to maintain. Unlike cattle and other species, if turned out on sufficient acreage, goats will ferret out the most nutritious forbs and browse, maintaining their higher nutritional needs without costly input by the farmer. That's still true today for most goats. Furthermore, there's a market, mostly an ethnic population, which will come directly to the farm and buy every one of these low input goats. Certainly, that almost seems too good to be true.

But now, so the argument goes, we have the high dollar, valuable imported goats and their offspring. Most of these goats have been pen raised on small acreage with lots of grain. I don't blame those folks for trying to protect their investment. After all, a thirty-five thousand dollar goat would make a mighty expensive snack for a hungry coyote. But it seems to me that we need to remember that those South African and New Zealand wonders were purportedly bred to survive like our native Spanish goats, under range conditions. That being the case, it is only a matter of a couple of years before the commercial ranchers can have the commercial offspring of those imports running on range and thriving on forage, no doubt as God and their founding breeders meant for them to do.

There will still be the purebred breeder on small acreage pouring the sack feed to them, but there will soon be enough commercial ranchers raising goats the low input way. These will be goats with properly developed rumens, goats that can get out in the brush and hustle for the best nutrients, and come in off the range fat and sassy as a feedlot steer. Which brings me back to the question: why would anyone put goats in a feedlot and pour all that money into them when goats can feed themselves efficiently, letting the producer keep the profit instead of handing it over to the feed lot and grain companies?

I've heard the argument about the poor goats that travel all the way to New York City, lose weight and nearly die after a tortuous trip of several hours. Ideally all producers could sell all their stock within a couple hour drive from the farm. But let's assume we must take a trailer load of goats to New York City from the boonies. The shrink the goat experiences during that time is mostly rumen contents and water. It seems to me a decent receiving facility with clean water, good hay and minerals would be adequate to turn those goats around in a brief period of time. So why are we now talking about a feedlot?

Well, it's been said that we need to have a uniform set of goats with the same size carcass and that feeding goats to a certain weight might insure that. It's a well-established fact that a milk fed goat is probably the most desirable carcass. Just ask Dr. Frank Pinkerton who graded and selected five or six of what he thought was the best carcasses out of a group and then took some Muslim buyers into the meat locker to view the hanging carcasses. He asked them to pick the best five or six. (Remember, Frank, also known as The Goat Man, has forgotten more about goats than most of us will ever learn.) They walked right by Frank's pick of the lot and chose the lightest colored ones – the milk fed carcasses which represented those closest to coming off their dam. The color, not the weight or muscling, told them which carcasses were best.

Nevertheless, we are told that we need to be forward thinking and address IMPS (Institutional Meat Purchase Specifications) if we are going to advance in this new meat goat industry. Grading and packaging will demand uniformity in carcasses for value based marketing. That's what we've heard in the cattle business for some time but, in reality, not too many producers get the extra value for their efforts.

Still, let's assume we need a uniform carcass. With purebred herd sires, such as the Boer and Kiko, goat kids can be weaned at 100 days with great uniformity, heavier weaning weights, and virtually no inputs in the kid. The carcasses will dress out substantially heavier than traditional milk fed goats and still maintain the tenderness of a weanling. This is not just a theory but has been a modus operandi in New Zealand for some time. In many ways, New Zealand is light years ahead of us agriculturally. They have proven computer models that dictate their management plans. They have found that the most efficient and profitable way to raise sheep and goats is by caring for the dams and selling the offspring before any costs are incurred keeping them beyond weaning.

So, why do we think we need goat feedlots? Maybe all the talk about putting goat meat in the supermarket, if there were four plus million goats a year that could be slaughtered, has ignited the fever. Chevon could become the newest yuppie delight, low fat, politically correct. We goat ranchers might all become the next J. R. Ewings! Since grading systems are being researched at this very moment, it seems the only problem might be that we don't have the four million some goats. In fact, many of us may not live to see that day since it is projected to be several decades away. The last count I heard was that we have about 700,000 goats, not even enough to meet the expanding ethnic market pounding at our doors, willing to drive out to our farm, and hand over their hard earned cash for our forage finished goat or milk fed cabrito.

Certainly that's not reason enough to reject the feedlot concept. The cattle people have done it for years and we really can learn something from those folks. Putting livestock on feed must be the thing that the really serious rancher strives for. It sounds pretty good at the feed store or café to say "yeah, I've got 500 steers on feed right now in Nebraska." Well, imagine how great it would be to say you've got 5000 goats on feed. A man could stand tall with talk like that. Of course, the cattle market experiences some pretty dramatic cycles.

The average cattle producer only makes money a couple of years out of the typical ten-year cattle cycle. The other years are a wash or a loss. Most of the rancher's costs are fixed with the exception of grain costs which are at their highest often when cattle prices are at their lowest. The most amazing thing is that the price of beef at the supermarket doesn't change significantly. The rancher can see the prices for his calves go from $1.25 per pound to nearly $0.25 per pound but a pound of ground round stays the same. It doesn't take a rocket scientist or computer nerd to figure that all the profit is going somewhere else besides into the producer's pocket.

I think that a little sack feed has its place in raising goats. It's good to use to get 'em back through the neighbor's fence to home or to call 'em up to work them. Maybe a little corn to flush the does before breeding is wise or perhaps just for making a social call to the pasture and having a little time to commune one on one with your goats is worth the price of a little grain. Beyond that, the feed sack is the vehicle of self-destruction.

Historically many practices in American agriculture have led the farmer into economic slavery. The new goat rancher has a chance to ride out of this bondage on the back of the new goat industry. He can do this by raising a low input commodity that is adept at harvesting weeds, grown with the energy from free sunlight, profitably. The corollary to this is to target the market directly. There are many outstretched hands willing to help market goats for a price. After all the prices are paid, will anything be left for the producer?

Goats can feed themselves on green growing stuff better than we could ever dream of meeting their needs with something out of a bag or feedlot. Every time something new comes around in sustainable agriculture, there's a team of specialists waiting in line to charge you for their services. We goat ranchers do need to hang together but maybe we don't need all of those specialists helping us raise goats. After all, if it ain't broke, don't fix it.

CHAPTER TWENTY-SIX

The Magic is Life on the Farm

Wintering livestock is not just expensive and labor intensive. It can seem like a daily assault on the corpus. Carrying feed sacks, hoisting square bales, slogging through the mud, making endless trips between the barn and pasture all take its toll. When we return from the cold and wet pasture to the warmth of the kitchen to seek the comfort of a hot cup of brew, we are looking for an ibuprofen chaser. Pulled muscles aching, joints creaking, stiffness setting in like readi-mix cement on a hot, dry day makes one wonder what is meant by the golden years. Do we work and save all our lives to retire to or finally buy the farm only to find that our youthful bodies, full of energy and optimism have been left behind in another time zone while we remain to re-invent the agrarian dream? Well, maybe not.

For all the discomfort we may encounter, we are nourished by our daily contact with the earth and its creatures. We have something money can't buy. We have the magic that comes from stewarding land and animals. In the book *Re-Enchantment of Everyday Life,* author Thomas Moore said "I worry about our civilization losing its farms, not because we need food grown on small farms – although that is true, too – but because we need the *spirit* of the farm in our midst." He also quotes poet Wendell Berry who has said, "You cannot have a post-agricultural world that is not also post-democratic, post-religious, and post-natural – in other words it will be, as we have understood ourselves, post-human."

The driving force keeping families in farming and ranching today is a quest for that relationship with nature. Sometimes we call it lifestyle but what we really mean is the quality of life, freedom and independence that comes with loving the land. The challenge lies in making the farm "pencil".

If improving our financial status was our only concern, most of us who farm or ranch could find other ways to invest our assets, time and talent. However, most of us that have been around awhile have also discovered that money, at best, is only a tool. Nevertheless, some degree of financial success is necessary if we want to continue living in our chosen farming or ranching vocation. The only real control that we, as farmers and ranchers, have are our expenses. Market prices, weather, politics and other factors may play a heavy hand in the final price we receive for our product. We can't influence those forces but we can make choices not to spend money or to manage in ways that contribute constructively to our bottom line.

The Amish Community represents an agricultural alternative and one we may learn much from in our quest for sustainability. The Amish farmer has the same twenty-four hours in each day that we do; he farms in the same economy with the same dollar. He does it largely by himself, notwithstanding community barn-raising efforts and such, on generally 150 acres or less and has been doing this successfully since the early 1800s.

Amish farmer, minister and author, David Kline, spoke at a Stockman Grass Farmer Conference in Jackson, Mississippi. He said many things about how the Amish farm works, emphasizing the importance of experience and tradition over scientific knowledge. He noted the importance of supporting the local community by not exporting money out of it. David also believes that the religious focus of their community contributes greatly to their success.

One chord that was struck loud and clear to me was the obvious harmony and balance with nature the Amish have achieved. Soil fertility, legumes and manure are almost revered as holy, as so it should be. By caring for the soil, we care for our crops and our animals and ultimately for our own soul. The Amish say, "if you sell hay or grain, you sell fertility. If you sell beef or milk, you sell water." Beware of what goes off your land.

A penchant to gravitate toward the organic pervades the Amish community. Generally only light applications of 12-12-12 might be used on corn otherwise they depend upon their legumes to fix nitrogen. They feed their soils with the manure from their livestock and occasionally apply lime as needed.

The Amish succeed because there is much self-sufficiency as well as an ethic that deplores waste and excesses. David said that one of their old sayings is that "a barn will build a house but a house will never build a barn." In the Amish community, you will not see the rural estate, as Alan Nation calls it, where there is a large mansion, fancy barns, facilities, pipe fences and expensive tractors and equipment. Such estates require a large input of outside cash and are not built from the proceeds of the farm. David said that all of his farm equipment could "fit inside a new John Deere with enough money left to go to Patagonia".

In his book *Becoming Native to This Land*, Wes Jackson makes the statement that "At some level, most of us want to live within our means, to become native to this place…" He goes on to say "in this world now dominated by economic thought, we have discovered that comfort and security are not solutions to the human condition and that affluence has not solved the economic problem. In fact, economic anxiety has increased."

David Kline says his secret is really very simple: Don't Spend Money. He admits that he's very tight but at the same time he'll tell you what a wonderful life they live. There is such joy in experiencing the seasons and harvest, tending the animals and sharing the community of friends and family with whom they have common goals. He pooh-poohs the perception that the Amish are extremely hard working. There's plenty of time to relax, he says "the farmer is the most undisciplined person because what he does depends on the weather."

Another tip for sustainability was to have more than one product or skill to offer. David said, "If you have great diversity, you are never in trouble." Our efforts to add meat goats to our farms will give us a more diversified agrarian base from which to operate. Preferring forbs and browse, goats do not compete with cattle for grass and can increase the grass by eliminating competing weeds. Goats also target a different market than the beef market. In addition, they are constantly sprinkling those time release fertilizer pellets around the pasture.

The new meat goat industry offers us a chance to become sustainable by diversifying and supplying a product that is greatly in demand. It may be our best shot at making the farm pencil while allowing us to care for our souls as well as for our finances. David Kline's stated goal in life is "to be useful". To be useful and to live in harmony with nature may be a state of grace and our aches and pains serve only to remind us that we are human.

CHAPTER TWENTY-SEVEN

Cattlemen versus Goat Ranchers

Each decade has its benchmarks. The roaring '20s saw nickel beer, the Model T and the legitimacy of mechanized farming. The '30 suffered through the depression and the great Dust Bowl, the '40s endured World War II and applauded women in the workforce to be followed by the post war boom of the '50s and an agricultural policy of feeding surplus grain to livestock. The '60s knew hippies, free love and the beginnings of the mother earthers who made attempts to return to the land on into the '70s while consumerism rose to new heights. The baby boomers came on big time in the '80s followed by the X-generation of the '90s where mutual funds, spiritual growth, environmental concerns, and folks coming out of the closet exploded.

As we begin the new millennium, we goat ranchers can expect to see a new twist in agricultural milestones. Formerly staunch cattlemen will be stepping forward confessing that they've joined the *fastest growing segment of US agriculture* – meat goat ranching.

While the West was being won in the early days of our country, the division between sheep raisers and cattle ranchers was distinct and often violent. There is presently a similar schism between much of the cattle industry and goat ranchers. It is a subtle phenomenon but one fraught with uneasiness, embarrassment and true confessions.

I have noticed that when I visit the local feedstore, a look of quiet desperation seems to wash over the face of the man behind the counter when I ask a question or start talking about my goat needs. He may be hoping I'll hurry and be on my way so that no one hears this interchange lest they label him a goat sympathizer. My cattlemen friends have exhibited varying reactions to my suggestion they consider adding goats. There is the nervous laughter, excuses about fencing inadequacies and the change-the-subject maneuver. But I've seen it before so I understand.

I know of a lady who raises goats profitably. After watching her success for several years, her father-in-law, who had been losing money in cattle, got some goats but made her promise not to breathe a word of it to any of his cattle friends. He had seen his cattleman son return home from the local sale barn miffed because he'd been called "goat boy".

We made a deliberate effort to invite cattlemen to a goat field day held at our ranch. We sent complimentary passes and press passes to livestock and beef publications, extension agents and feed store managers. Not too many of them were used nor were we that surprised. There was a tremendous turnout of serious goat ranchers and we found that very satisfying. We were flooded with enthusiastic calls and e-mails from goat folks who genuinely enjoyed the field day and the outstanding slate of speakers. We even discovered that some of the people who attended were closet goat ranchers, cattlemen not quite ready to go public with goats.

Gary Harding from Connors State College, in Warner, Oklahoma delivered a message with which many attendees could identify. Gary teaches livestock management and conducts the popular Connors bull tests and sales well known to Oklahoma cattlemen. Gary began his talk with the confession that not so long ago he would have been embarrassed for his cattlemen peers to know he was spending the day attending a goat seminar. Gary has become a convert since he discovered the benefit goats provide in improving Eastern Oklahoma pastures for the cattle.

Although Connors does not have a research program, observations in pastures grazed by goats noted an increase in grass, decrease in greenbriar, poison ivy, winged elm, honey locust, and western and lanceleaf ragweed and elimination of wild roses, blackberry bushes and red cedar. Concurrently the population of the American Burying Beetle has more than doubled as shown by a beetle-trapping program to monitor their population within the grazed area.

Our Moorman Dealer, Greg Weems from Stigler, Oklahoma, attended the seminar. Greg is also a longtime cattleman, savvy in bovine nutrition, who has been observing the emerging meat goat industry from the wings. He came to the field day with Charles Fitzgerald, a fellow Moorman dealer from Talihina, Oklahoma. Charles has a few goats himself and has been telling Greg about the benefits. So between Charles' interest and our invitation and urging, Greg came out for the field day.

I guess it was the evening of the next day when Greg called the house. He thanked us profusely for our part in hosting the field day and complimented the speakers. He also said that he'd been "held hostage by weed sprayers and brushhogs" but now he could see some alternatives and stated, "you've just about converted me." Greg even gave me permission to quote him.

Cattleman Red Smith of Morven, Georgia is well known in goat circles for his experience in running large numbers of goats and cattle. Red said, "we wanted to add something to our cattle operation and after fighting weeds and brush for 30 years, we decided to give goats a try. We used a bush hog mower in Georgia, Marden choppers in Florida and machetes in Belize, Ca. We have found now that we can utilize the weeds and brush to our advantage with goats. Now, instead of fighting the weeds and brush, we manage them. I was really surprised to find out that there is much more food value in weeds and brush than in most grasses. We now manage our brush, weeds and grasses for the benefit of our goats (browsers) and cattle (grazers)." The strongest testimonial a cattleman could give for using goats has to be Red's statement: "The cattle will have to go too if we get out of goats."

There will be more interest among cattlemen in the future as they see our pastures improve without costly herbicides, and as they see us produce more pounds of meat per acre and receive more income than is possible running only cattle.

Anyone who has been in the cattle business over the last five years knows how bad the price of calves has been. We use our livestock to harvest the grass and forbs grown by free sunlight. As producers, we are paid by the pound. After accounting for expenses, the price per pound and the number of pounds we produce per acre is the bottom line.

In a best case scenario, based on realistic prices, if a producer weans a 500 pound calf, in a grass based program where one acre carries one cow/calf pair as one animal unit, and sells the calf at $100/CWT, then he would gross $500 per acre.

If that same producer ran ten does per acre (instead of one cow) and averaged a 200% kid crop, and the twins sold at 100 days weighing a reasonable 45 pounds, then he would be producing 900 pounds per acre. At comparable liveweight prices of $.65 to $.79 per pound that would be a gross figure of $585 to $711 per acre.

If that same producer kept his cows and ran six does per acre with his cows, he'd have an additional 540 pounds of meat goats to sell in addition to his calf that would bring him an additional $351 to $426. Now we are talking about grossing close to $1,000 per acre with multi-species grazing of goats and cattle. Even when adjusted down to a 150% kid crop, six does per acre with cattle should produce an additional $263 to $320 per acre over the gross income from the calf.

Historically most major changes are driven by climatic and economic considerations. We won't propel the goat industry to the forefront because goats are charming critters on the farm or because they make our pastures look more picturesque. Goat ranching will become big business because there is the potential to make a handsome profit while servicing an *existing market*.

In the future the chagrined cattlemen's interest will grow into desire and commitment to be followed by pride as their profit grows. One by one they'll be coming out of the closet. Converted cattlemen will become diverse grass-based agrarians operating in a more sustainable mode.

And do you know what else? Just maybe there'll be more family farms that can make it in America. Perhaps we will live to see the re-birth of the family farm in this new millennium, thanks to goat ranching and grass farming. Sort of makes you feel like a pioneer, doesn't it?

CHAPTER TWENTY-EIGHT

Keep On Keepin'
On Thankfully

As if a prelude to Thanksgiving, October and November is a splendid time of year in the foothills of the Ouchita Mountain Range of Southeastern Oklahoma. Endless days of brutal heat and humidity give way to crisp mornings, friendly sunshine and suppers after dark. We feel a sense of satisfaction as the last of the green tomatoes become relish and the hay equipment is put up for the winter. But during 1998 there wasn't any garden and the hay equipment never made it to the field. That was the year of the drought.

Although too late for many, the rain and new growth finally came only to be followed by invasions of armyworms, moving silently in mass, decimating pastures everywhere. Ranchers who had managed to keep some livestock through the summer gave up and hauled cows, calves and goats alike to the auction barn, taking whatever salvage price they brought. We felt lucky that our goats had the timber to rescue them from forsaken pastures. They made it through the summer, maybe not as bloomy looking as usual, but in relatively good shape. Even so, it was a tough year for family farms everywhere with prospects for wintering looking gloomy.

It had been the kind of year that forces you to reexamine your goals. Although some think it should, the bottom line alone can't tell a farmer what he needs to do. Farming and ranching has always been challenged to remain in the black. Some would say that the term 'profitable farming' is an oxymoron. The complexities of biology and weather are wild cards in planning ahead. Even when the market appears stable and the farmer can estimate his production costs, they are rarely more than a best guess.

Too many family farms fail. While they lose their footing, they use up their off farm earnings along with every last liquid asset to stay on the farm. Unlike most careers, losing your farm means more than just losing a job. It represents the loss of heart, home and a way of life. Attempts to hang on arise from a deep well of desire to remain on the land because we are a part of the land and the land is a part of us. Our fabrics are woven together so tightly that to remove or damage one tears at the other. To stay on the land, cash on hand is spent, then the savings or retirement funds, maybe an inheritance, next the capital assets are sold off piece by piece to keep going. Cannibalizing itself, the farm fails.

Outsiders, from urban relations to financial advisors, may seem puzzled by this phenomenon but what they are witnessing is the refusal of the pioneer spirit to die. The family farm is more than a vocation. It represents independence tied to the land and the seasons as well as an opportunity to live authentically. For many, it is the only acceptable way of life.

This country was settled by pioneer families who valued the freedom to live and work their own piece of earth and direct the course of their own lives. This is our heritage. It comes to us through more than history alone. With all the new research and speculation about intelligence on a cellular level, we should not be surprised that this spirit, this drive, this memory might survive today in our own DNA, pushing us to continue farming when common sense says "no more".

It's doubly hard today. I've heard older people raised during the depression of the 1930s say that they didn't know they were poor growing up. Everyone was poor in their world. The media of today that has brought us together to the table of instant communication has made us aware of the possibilities. We want the good life with all the consumer options available. Herein lies the rub. Farm families of today won't accept the poverty and spartan standard of living that allowed so many in the past to make it on the farm. We want the latest electronics, pizzas delivered, wide screen TV, second cars, lessons and extra-curricular activities for the children, vacations and more.

The irony of it all is that while the American farmer has more capital investment than the average non-farm worker, he often has a lower visible standard of living. His earned dollars are not buying the latest model car, upgraded homes, swimming pools or country club memberships. They are being reinvested into maintaining the farm, feeding livestock, repairing equipment, making payments to the bank on enterprises that frequently cannot repay the debt they have created. Although he may be rich in intangibles, during years like 1998, there will be little to no profit from the farm. More likely, there will be more debt incurred. The challenges today are greater as the modern farm family tries to live along side their suburban counterpart, reaching for similar amenities and lifestyle while maintaining the homestead.

Personal sacrifice comes in more than one way. Farmers are not only on call twenty-four hours a day, they are often without paid vacation, matching fund pension plans, IRAs & subsidized health care, unless their off farm jobs can provide some of it. While the years slip by, the farmer is getting older and feeling his limitations. Then there comes a year like this one.

But, one more Thanksgiving rolled around and as I grumbled about the weather, the losses, vertical integration, middlemen and monopolies, I remembered a line out of "Rancher's Rights" by Bob Kingsbery, which says:

"Ranchers have the right to the special satisfaction that comes from providing a valuable service to society and devoting their lives to caring for their land and livestock."

So we'll continue to give thanks for the right to ranch, for the family and friends we love, and for the gift of life and all its possibilities. And one more thing, we'll give thanks for those charming little critters called goats.

Cattle and goats are a good multi-species combo.
Goats eat the weeds and cattle eat the grass.

Kiko goats forage brush during a severe drought.

CHAPTER TWENTY-NINE

Fields of Goats and Agrarian Dreams

A couple of years ago I was killing time in the new arrivals section of a bookstore while my friend was perusing the used CD's when *Fields Without Dreams* by Victor Davis Hanson seemed to leap out from the shelves into my arms. I thought that I really didn't have time to read a book then. A full off-farm work day, ranch management by phone, and my other goat related activities pretty much used up my 24 hours each day. But, the subtitle: defending the agrarian idea cinched it.

Papa and I had been working desperately the previous decade defending our agrarian idea to get to the point of full time ranching. We had poured every dollar we could scrounge into the ranch in hopes of fulfilling our dream of creating a diversified, sustainable, agricultural operation in our lifetime.

We had called it a ranch since the day we came back to find an overgrown scrubby oak and pine patch of ground dotted with small meadows that we called pastures, in spite of the fact that there were more greenbrier, broomsage and sumac than bermuda or native grasses. Some of the locals laughed at our reference to a bunch of rocks and timber as a ranch. Perhaps they had long since given up their dreams and believed we too would soon fall in line with the defeated American farmer. But, we had fields of dreams on which to focus and as the sand runs out of the hour glass of our lives, we find we are more committed to our agrarian vision.

Hanson's book is a bitter, angry, yet brutally honest tale of the demise of much of their five-generation California raisin farm. Through ill weather, falling prices, surplus and deflation, corrupt cooperatives, ruthless commission buyers, mammoth agri-business and vertical integration, high input of chemical herbicides and pesticides, Hanson shows us that "the real problem…for all farmers in America now…is never the inability to grow food but always the bounty and the falling price driven down by the ability to do so."

Hanson, a farmer and Greek scholar, eloquently illustrates the basic fact in agriculture today that the producer, for all his capital investment, risk taking, and sacrifice to home and health, is on the bottom of the food chain, taking the smallest share of the final selling price while all the middle men reap the fat. He further makes the point that our Western society has its roots in the Greek City State. The agrarian values that emerged as the foundation of Greek society later became the basis of our democratic agrarian western culture.

Hanson proposes that as we lose the family farm, which is now less than 1% of our populous, we will lose both a wisdom and work ethic derived from ancient Greece. He postulates that if we lose this value and work ethic, we will see increasing chaos and violence in our society. He notes that "it still is rare to find in modern America anyone who will pay in currency and health to have a lifetime free of nodding 'yes'." The agrarian today, like the Greek yeoman, tends to be moral, self-reliant, conservative in his political views and driven by a purpose tied to the land and the seasons. Big business can buy low and sell high but Hanson points out that the farmer cannot, for it is not simply a business but a stewardship with responsibilities and ties to ancestral land.

Hanson's book made me think about other areas of agriculture besides vineyards and orchards, such as poultry farming and cattle ranching. I remember talking with a new goat rancher whose chicken houses were costing him $41 per day out of his own pocket for the privilege of taking care of the chickens and the facility, mortgaging everything he owned to the bank and living in virtual economic slavery. No doubt he hoped that raising meat goats might provide some relief.

The price of cattle has been disastrous the past few years and many herds have been liquidated and farms lost. The producer, receiving half the price his calves brought five years ago, still faces the same and higher expenses. But the pitiful prices paid to the beef cattle rancher is not reflected in the supermarket where the price of beef has varied little. So what are we to think in this era of high-priced grain, except that the feeders, packers and grain monopoly maintain their profit levels at the expense of the producer. It is always the American producer who takes the hit.

A vast majority of the new goat ranchers of today are people who are exercising an option for either an alternative agricultural venture or even a complete career change. In many cases they are cattle producers who have put a pencil to the dollar per acre to be realized with goats versus cattle. In some cases it is the traditional farmer who must subsidize his farm with employment in town while he hopes to substitute meat goat production for the off farm job.

We producers are witnessing the growth of a new meat goat industry whose size and scope will far exceed the historical Spanish brush goat and Fourth of July cabrito.

The market is growing and we must strive to protect ourselves from the middlemen who would take all our profit while we offer all our lifeblood, time and capital to produce an excellent product. We must insist that government subsidies do not find their way into meat goat ranching. Hanson contends that "the growth in size of the Department of Agriculture is commensurate with the decline of the family farmer."

He also warns us to maintain vigilance over cooperatives lest they be transformed from a unified arm of producers into a bureaucratic monster demanding high salaries for varied full-time positions and draining the profits meant for the owner, the farmer and rancher.

If Victor Davis Hanson is historically correct in stating that we are in the throes of death of the family farm, "in the third stage of a future that has no future, an agrarian Armageddon at the millennium where the family farm itself – both as a way of life and a reassuring image of the mind – will be obliterated," then perhaps our small meat goat segment of agriculture can maintain the family farm, serving both as a model and a reminder of a better world.

PART SIX

Hindsight
and the Rest
of the Story

July 1999: The smoldering aftermath
of the fire on Caston Creek.

Temporary catch pens can be set up easily
in timbered and other hard to reach areas.

The Rest
of the Story

At the height of our goat involvement we faced the reality of downsizing our operation due to health concerns. Then about the time we had adjusted physically and emotionally to the fact that we weren't as young as we used to be, our home burned. And as I have done my entire life, I wrote about these events. Those pieces appeared in newsprint and are included in this section which is perhaps fittingly called "the rest of the story".

After the fire we returned to our previous careers in the oil patch and found ourselves exploring Wyoming and the Northwest before returning to Texas to work. During an extended stay with our oldest daughter in Colorado, I wrote "Maddie", a middle grade novel, which was my grief work after leaving the farm. It is a story about a twelve year girl who tries to convince her dad to raise goats to eat the weeds instead of using dangerous chemicals to eliminate them. "Maddie" is planned as the first in a series that I hope to finish in the coming years.

While we continued to perform petroleum land work, my thoughts and interest remained on the farm and we stayed in touch with many of our neighbors and friends. One of our ranching friends who also raised meat goats was trapped in an adhesion contract with a local poultry company. He was not the only one. For years I had listened to tales of abuse from area poultry farmers. When our friend joined other farmers in a lawsuit against the company, I knew it was time to tell this tale. After months of exhausting research and interviewing farmers around the country, I wrote a fact-based fictional novel called "Plucked and Burned".

One of the most poignant moments of the research and book touring was when we met a young widow of a poultry farmer who had committed suicide after being 'plucked and burned' by the company. Her story is included here as well to help serve as a warning to all farmers and lovers of the agrarian dream to beware of the smooth seduction from mega-agriculture that is fraught with moguls devoid of ethics – and to serve as a reminder that alternative farming ventures exist that offer independence and profit. Diversification and raising meat goats is one healthy step in the right direction.

During the creation of "Plucked and Burned", the characters became my daily friends with a life of their own. Perhaps this should not be surprising since many were a composite of real people. One that I found most endearing was a character named Red Hensley, a big gruff guy with a heart of gold who runs goats with Anatolian Shepherds and carries a small mongrel dog around in the bib of his overalls. For fun, I've included a selection here about Red.

Last, but I hope not least, I've included a piece which appeared in the Summer 2001 issue of "Farming Magazine" out of Amish country in Mt. Hope Ohio. The wisdom of hindsight and the merits of a more objective perspective influence this article that is in many ways a distillation of what we learned about raising goats.

Now, almost seven years after the fire, I am immersed in building a publishing company, as well as a life, and I expect good things to happen. And, what about Caston Creek Ranch? It still awaits our return. From time to time our children come and pitch a tent along the creek and drop a line into the water. A neighbor runs cattle in the pastures and cuts hay from the fields. Instead of tending critters, I look after three Jack Russell Terriers and know that come what may, life does go on.

Will we return to Caston Creek? Time will tell. But surely the love of the land and its place in our agrarian dreams will bring us home. And, that's the rest of the story for now.

CHAPTER THIRTY

Caston Creek Chronicles

June 1999 – Just a Turn in the Road

I guess that before we are even born we are assigned a path to travel in this life along which our destiny will push or lead us to the final destination. We rarely know what lies very far ahead although we often think we do. Sometimes we catch a glimpse from a reflective moment and imagine how things might be different. Sometimes we plan our lives far in advance quite certain that we can control the outcome of events and reach our goals. But more often than not, we find ourselves in circumstances far different from what we had planned and as unique and original as any we might have conjured up as belonging to someone else.

Sometimes a radical change in direction is not always what we think we want or need. But, true happiness comes from accepting the hand that life has dealt us and looking for the blessings that are hidden in every crisis. Unexpected change at first blush can masquerade as adversity but upon closer examination we can find the gifts that such challenges bring. Like Jimmy Buffet sings in his "Beach House on the Moon" Album,

"Sometimes the best map will not guide you. You can't see what's round the bend. Sometimes the road leads through dark places. Sometimes the darkness is your friend."

I was certain when we moved to Caston Creek that it would be my final stop. Now, due to physical limitations and other family needs, we find ourselves dispersing our animals and the ranch's heavy metal. As the Millennium plus one arrives, Papa will be pushing seventy years of age and has decided it's time to slow down and smell the roses. We both agree that he's earned it. We will be keeping a few goats and considering a retirement farm closer to the grandkids. For us it's time to give up the large ranching operation in exchange for more time with family and friends. It's time to trade long days filled with the likes of fixing fences and equipment, wrestling livestock and making hay for a more relaxed pace. Maybe a garden and a few laying hens, and of course a couple of goats, will see us through the next turn in the road.

My new book *"The Meat Goats of Caston Creek,"* now at the printer, will soon be out. It has been a labor of love as I've shared our memoir along the learning curve in raising meat goats. I hope that it will help people, especially newcomers, to gain a perspective on goat ranching that will lead them to a successful endeavor. I have said that without the agrarian experience and the discovery of goats, there would be no such book. I am grateful for having had that experience. I carry with me many wonderful memories and images of scenes too beautiful to describe.

This newest twist and turn in our path was not met without a few tears. But, now our eyes are dry and we are looking joyfully forward to the new adventure that lies before us. We see it as an opportunity to re-invent our agrarian dream, to shape it into one that will accommodate this season of our lives. We realize that it's just another turn in the road and not the end of the journey. We're not going too far away. Old goat ranchers never die, they just move on to greener pastures.

CHAPTER THIRTY-ONE

Coping with Loss
on Caston Creek

T he Lord giveth and the Lord taketh away. We are born into this world with nothing and we leave with nothing. And nothing lasts forever. Sometimes life reminds us of this in less than gentle ways. On July 27th of this year (1999) Papa and I along with our New Zealand friend, goat consultant Graham Culliford, awoke from a deep sleep to several loud unidentifiable thuds. My mind stumbled through its memory banks trying to identify the intruding assault to my half-awakened senses. I shook my sleeping husband and said, "Steve, someone is trying to break in." How much easier that would have been.

I glanced at the clock and saw that it was 5:28 am. Within seconds we were forced to recognize through our disoriented half-awake state that our home was on fire. The horrible reality descending on us was that a fire had spread beneath the floor and through the roof, totally engulfing the backside of the house, blowing in bedroom windows and sending flames high into the air. Fueled by ruptured propane lines, it burned like an oilfield fire.

I stood for a few moments, time frozen in my distorted awareness. I looked at the picture frames filled with babies lining the top of my dresser.

Fire and loss on Caston Creek

I thought of the journals that lay in the bottom drawers chronicling our years of agrarian struggle. I remembered the remnants and memoirs from my father's estate, family heirlooms and the volumes of business records and database every family business builds over a lifetime. I tried to deny the possibility that I would not be able to return to claim these treasures.

The men's shouts that we must "get out now" overcame my mind's denial. I grabbed the slacks I had pulled off at bedtime, my purse and briefcase that occupied their usual spot beside my bed, and ran out into the yard. I in my nightgown, Papa barefoot in his underwear, and Graham half dressed, we moved the vehicles away from the blazing house. Less than two or three minutes had passed from the time we were awakened until we exited the house. There had been no time to process what was happening much less retrieve any valuables.

We watched as the volunteer fire fighters struggled to bring the fire under control. They nearly had the fire subdued when they ran out of water. The house burned to the ground before they could return with the pumper unit refilled.

But things can be replaced, human life snuffed out is irretrievable. Yes, there are sentimental losses that tug at the heart. There is incredible nuisance in trying to rebuild the records and structure within which we maintain our daily lives. There are demons that bump around inside the psyche when the rational mind is ready to move on. But we are in awe of the fact that we escaped, surviving to tell this tale. Our children tell us our duty now is to live long enough to make more memories.

I have raised children and livestock and have seen my share of hard times, illness, blood and guts and believed I could think on my feet pretty well. But this experience of being awakened from a deep sleep with only seconds to evaluate and react to a crisis that the mind does not want to accept, has convinced me of the need for families to conduct fire drills. It is especially important for families with small children or those living in mobile homes. Families should discuss routes of escape depending on the origination of the fire.

Every family member should know where to find the number to the fire department. I flipped through the first five pages of our local phone book and I couldn't find the number – by then I was out of time. If the number had been posted on the phone or written in big bold letters on the cover or inside of the book, I might have been able to make a quick call and shorten the interval before the volunteers arrived. Our neighbors did call a few minutes later but I will always wonder if five minutes might have made a difference. If you have practiced for this thing that we all think happens to "other people" and there is a fire, not only will your children kick into "auto pilot" and know what to do, so will you.

Farmers and ranchers have the extra challenge of preparing for the possibility of a fire in barns housing livestock. I spoke recently with a young lady who had lost two show calves and a sow with her litter of show pigs in a barn fire. It was very traumatic for the entire family, not to mention the financial loss. She said they did not have any alternate or emergency exits. When penning animals that rely on you to provide for their safety, it might be worth thinking about constructing some escape hatches. It's always handy anyway to have more than one avenue for moving animals about.

A friend offered the reminder that the Lord doesn't give us more than we can handle. Another said, "when bad things happen to good people, it's the Universe preparing the way for better things to come." Another acknowledged the personal and devastating nature of a fire that destroys a home and said, "maybe in the long run it will turn out to be a blessing." Maybe. God doesn't let me in on all of His secrets. But, right now I can relate best to the greeting card with the sad looking basset hound on the front and the words: "They say you learn the most from your most difficult experiences. What a stupid system."

Spanish and Boer Cross Goats were part of our commercial mix.

These Kiko crosses hustle for groceries in the timber.

CHAPTER THIRTY-TWO

The High Price of Cheap Chicken in America

T he high price of cheap chicken in America lies neither in the constantly evolving miracle of modern technology nor in the research labs of land grant colleges, rather it is the growing toll of human life and the destruction of family farms that buys our modern meal. Jimmy Johnson was forty-nine years old when he became another statistic for contract poultry growing, another canary in the mines of industrial agriculture. The father of two teenaged boys, the husband of his childhood sweetheart, he decided the only option left for him was suicide.

We stopped by the church cemetery to look at Jimmy's headstone. We promised his widow, Sheralyn, we would; she said it was easy to spot. Glistening like black ice in sunlight, it was immediately visible. The Johnson family name, carved into the dark granite stone, stood out amid decades of gray monuments representing theirs and other families in the small farming community. We paused for several minutes, quietly nursing our own private thoughts as to why this young husband and father became yet another victim of contract agriculture. No simple answers came.

I walked around to the opposite side of the marker, caught the first glimpse of its etchings and the hair on my arms stood up as my heart lurched. "By love we three were wed, we and the land are one," it said beneath a scene that lovingly depicted the family's homestead complete with the outline of their house and a tractor in the fields. If I had any doubt as to what drives farmers like Jimmy to choose suicide as the only alternative to losing the farm, this simple statement spoke volumes.

Mary Clouse, former grower and retired Director of Contract Reform for the Rural Advancement Foundation International (RAFI-USA) accompanied us to the graveyard at Hickory Mountain Baptist Church. She later had this to say about the inscription on Jimmy Johnson's headstone: "The lines express the essence of family farming - farmers so wedded to their land that when torn from it by falling farm prices or new corporate farming schemes that use up farmers then cast them aside, some may not survive the separation." Mary also pointed out that we should ask ourselves, "who will be so in love with the land that they will take such good care of it, if not the family farmer?"

According to Dr. C. Robert Taylor, Alfa Eminent Scholar and Professor of Agricultural Economics at Auburn University, today's chicken farmers put up over 50% of the capital required to produce a marketable chicken. Their supposed partner, the chicken company, puts up less than 50% yet reaps the lion's share of the profit; and we are talking lion and field mouse divisions here. Traditionally poultry integrators have posted 20-30% profits while poultry farmers might show a 1-2% return on investment (ROI). The reality is that most growers are making a negative ROI when a value is put on time and labor.

The spin doctors for the chicken companies, such as Richard Lobb, Director of Communications for the National Chicken Council, Washington DC, justify the low or negative ROI by making such statements as, "...there is no basis whatsoever for saying that 45 percent of growers live on $15,000 or less...37 percent of growers had off-farm jobs and 65 percent had farm operations other than broilers." (Excerpted from public posts on the Internet's Yahoo Broiler List about a survey performed circa 2000.) So are we to conclude that it is okay to cheat your 50% partner if they can work additional off-farm jobs or raise other things besides chickens?

While the Bush administration focuses on foreign terrorism, it follows in the steps of those who have gone before by turning a blind eye to the corporate terrorism that is an every day occurrence on many of America's family farms. Attempts to pass legislation to restore competitive markets, to put muscle into GIPSA (Grain Inspectors Packers & Stockyards Administration) to enforce existing laws or to level the playing field for family farmers, is met by high powered lobby efforts, disinformation and the veiled threat that the industry could pull out of the state in question and go elsewhere.

Ten years ago poultry farmers rose up, organized in state and national associations, and rallied to improve the plight of the chicken farmer. Steve Bjerklie, respected editor of Meat Processing Magazine, wrote a three part series called "Dark Passages" in which he said, " ...the possibility of a cave-in at the deepest point of poultry's vertical integration demands coverage because reverberations from such a disaster would shoot straight up through the entire shaft of the industry." Part three of the series, in the December 1994 issue, focused on "efforts to resolve what has become an increasingly acrimonious situation", Steve had this to say: "In some cases, these new efforts follow efforts made 20 or even 30 years ago to redress grower complaints. Those earlier attempts at reform did not produce any new laws or action; that will not be the case this time, however."

Steve won the coveted 1995 award for best series of articles in a trade magazine from the Western Publications Association. He covered the topic succinctly and with honesty, fairness and accuracy in a publication that some might call the mouthpiece for integrators. Regrettably it is now nearly a decade later and still there have been no appreciable changes to benefit the victims of this industry.

The present situation has evolved out of the vertically integrated system introduced over fifty years ago. In its inception, vertical integration provided a more constant supply of commodity to market and was beneficial for both the chicken companies and the farmer. There were hundreds of family owned chicken companies who were basically farmers themselves. They worked hand in hand with the growers and the system was equitable and profitable for both.

However, over the course of half a century, the fine-tuning of vertical integration and worse yet, the consolidation of chicken companies has led to a morally degrading system where a few mega-corporations hold all the cards. Big Chicken likes to point out that there are forty or more chicken companies, but does not mention that Tyson, Pilgrim's Pride, and Goldkist control 48.1% of the market, followed by Perdue Farms, Wayne Farms (ContiGroup), Sanderson's Farms, and Cagle's which controls 18.3%, together comprising 66.4%. That market share plus the apparent tacit agreement to stay off of each other's turf, leaves the grower without the opportunity to choose a company for which to work and effectively eliminates a competitive market. The word on the street is that more companies are up got sale and will soon be swallowed up by the major players.

These moguls of agri-business appear to be driven by endless greed and desire for power. The competition to improve the bottom line, increase the value of stock options and support upper management's million dollar salaries is paramount. Efficiency in production is the catchword of the day and drives the effort to squeeze every sector of cost including the human factor. Ethics exist only in the ivory towers of university business programs, if there. Many poultry farmers, the capital investment partners of the industry, live in poverty calling themselves the last slaves to be freed in the South.

How can this happen in America? From what poultry growers have confided in me, it seems that most chicken farmers are scammed into the business. (I say confided because they speak on the grounds of anonymity; retaliation is a huge concern among growers . . but that is a topic for another time.) Believing that they have finally found a commodity that will pay enough to stay on the farm, they are promised good profits, great cash flow, and the opportunity to grow chickens for the rest of their lives. Many of these salt-of-the-earth farmers come from a southern culture of helping their neighbors and doing business on a handshake. They are not so jaded as to think the big brand names we see in the supermarkets could actually be operating Cosa Nostra style, disrespecting human life for the sake of pure power and profit. Once the lands are mortgaged for the high-priced poultry barns, the farmer is at the mercy of an integrator to keep him supplied with chickens to raise in order to pay his debt. Seldom does he realize beforehand that without control of any of these inputs, he is no more than an indentured servant.

The farmer furnishes the barns and his labor, 24/7. The poultry companies own the chickens and the feed that are delivered if, when and how the companies decide. The poultry companies inform the farmer that the dead chickens and the arsenic laden litter are his, effectively transferring any environmental liability to the unsuspecting poultry farmer.

Jimmy was a chicken farmer and like so many before him, mortgaged his family lands in order to build the expensive, single purpose, poultry barns required to raise broilers. He and his wife believed the promises the company made that it would provide a good living and eventually a good retirement. And predictably, Jimmy was forced to upgrade his equipment in order to continue receiving chickens. Poultry companies routinely force their growers to change out equipment or make major structural changes in poultry barns.

These upgrades require additional mortgages of tens of thousands of dollars. An upgrade of $100,000.00 is not uncommon and can be mandated so that the company might make a fraction of a cent more per pound by *maybe* improving feed conversion in a bird that has been genetically and chemically modified to achieve maximum growth in the minimum amount of time. Upgrades, paid for by the farmer, generally benefit only the company. Upgrades have such a poor track record in some parts of the country that area banks are refusing to finance them on the grounds that they do not pencil. Poultry growers claim that one of the main reasons upgrades are demanded by the companies is to keep them under their thumb. Apparently so.

Against his best judgment but in order to continue receiving chickens Jimmy met with the bank and arranged for financing to upgrade the existing poultry barns. He bit the bullet and took out another large mortgage to pay for the automated equipment that the company insisted he have. Before the note was signed, the existing equipment failed and a house of birds smothered. The company terminated Jimmy as a grower. They said he couldn't be trusted since he'd lost a house of birds. After his death, Jimmy's family sent the faulty alarm in to be analyzed. Strangely enough, the alarm was lost along with their opportunity to show that the loss was not due to Jimmy's negligence.

Jimmy's widow, Sheralyn, said, "If things had not happened the way they did I really believe that Jimmy would still be with us today. Our love for the farm and the life that we had made here was so great that he could not accept the thought of losing it. I truly believe that he gave his life so that we could stay here on the farm and so that our boys would have the opportunity to farm."

Jimmy was labeled a bad grower. I've been told that is what companies say when anything goes wrong. That if they deliver sick birds, or moldy feed, or feed with too much salt, or a load too late and feed conversion ratios are negatively affected, the farmer will be called a bad grower. Nothing is ever the company's fault. Accountability only runs in one direction. If the company decides it wants houses located within a closer radius of the processing plant, growers outside of that radius will probably find that they have forgotten how to raise birds. Or so they'll be told – bad growers, you know.

You might ask why people don't sue; we are such a litigious society. It so happens that the chicken farmers are called independent contractors. No matter that every move they make is choreographed by the company, delivered to them by a roving field service man, or written in stone in a grower manuals, subject to change by the company. In truth they are no more than underpaid (or never paid) employees without insurance and benefits or the ability to unionize. Kudos to the Oklahoma Attorney General for making that plain.

Still, operating under the charade of an independent contractor relationship, poultry companies tie the grower's hands with an adhesion contract, an agreement said to lie largely in the gray area between legal and illegal but generally considered not a legal contract. This adhesion contract is a take-it-or-leave it deal: Now that you have a million dollar mortgage, you take our deal or we leave you with the debt and no way to service it. And as if this contract, that can be terminated by the company at any moment, is not insult enough, they've added arbitration clauses after one or two growers across the nation successfully sued for fraud and racketeering. (Well, we can't have any more of that now can we?)

Arbitration sounds tame on the surface but the reality is that it's often more expensive than litigation and not appropriate where the chance of case setting precedent might exist. Arbitration favors any company that is the steady customer and has the opportunity to develop a relationship with the arbitrator, while each new farmer to come to the table is a stranger. Arbitration also deprives the plaintiff of discovery, a vital aspect of his right to civil redress.

So as poultry companies laugh about attempts to change legislation to favor family farmers, poultry farmers say they suffer retaliation at their hands for trying to organize, for talking to the media, for complaining about unfair treatment while their calls to GIPSA seem to fall on deaf ears. The message to farmers is loud and clear, we own you and we can make or break you. It effectively silences most of the complaints. Effective, efficient, and inhumane – corporate terrorism's legacy: the loss of America's family farms.

Anyone who has driven around the countryside can attest to the hundreds of empty chicken houses that stand as a testament to broken promises and shattered dreams. Unfortunately the high price of cheap chicken all too often includes the loss of life on the family farm. To Big Chicken, human lives are a disposable resource, but to the Johnson family the loss is priceless and forever. Rest in peace, Jimmy.

D'Artagnon

Babe, Pup and Jo

CHAPTER THIRTY-THREE

Who is Red Hensley?

From the moment he popped out out from between his mother's massive thighs and the country doctor announced, "Welcome to the world, Red," Aldous Hensley was known as 'Red'. At sixty-eight years of age, with a full head of iron red hair and a beard streaked with white and gray, he took care of four chicken houses by himself and ran a meat goat herd along with about fifty brood cows. He had been a widower for two years. Shortly after his wife's death, his oldest daughter thought it would be best for him to have a companion. She showed up at the farm one day with an eight-week-old puppy she had picked up at the animal shelter in Poteet. They thought it was part Chihuahua and part Pekinese but no one dared to venture a guess. It looked like the well-worn bristle end of a brown and black toilet brush and weighed about as much.

When Red saw it, he said, "Daughter, you take the damn dog back to the pound. I got enough to say grace over right here without wet nursin' a new pup."

But after she kissed him goodbye and drove off, he realized the dog was waiting for him on the top step of his front porch. The only reason he let the mutt in the house that night was because he was afraid the coyotes would make a snack of it and his daughter would never forgive him. But not a problem, he would see that she took it back.

As long as the dog had to stay a bit, he decided to go ahead and put a water and food bowl down in a corner by the stove. He opened the bag of puppy food the daughter had left and poured it into the dish. The little dog went to nibbling right away.

"Hungry, were you? Humph." Red retired to the living room and read the newspaper, watched a little TV and took the puppy outside to relieve herself before turning into bed.

"Well, Dog, what are we gonna do with you? Humph. I guess you can sleep on this here," he said, putting a clean old towel down near the bowls.

Aldous 'Red' Hensley was just starting to enter that luscious period of sleep when the body has finally relaxed and the mind begins to wander and process the problems of the day when he heard a whining, high pitched howl coming from beside his bed. The moonlight shone through his window across the worn oak floor onto a small bristly fur ball. He looked down and saw two sorrowful little eyes looking up at him.

"What's the matter, Dog? Miss your littermates? Okay, just for tonight," he said as he picked her up and set her on the foot of the bed.

The next morning Red awoke to find the dog nestled into the curve of his shoulder and neck, licking his face.

The rest is history. Dog continued to sleep in the bed and had the run of the house. By the time the daughter returned, Dog was a permanent fixture.

Dog followed Red around the house, she tried to go outside when he did, she cried for him when he left and displayed boundless joy upon his return. Tiny as she was, he nearly stepped on her half a dozen times before he discovered he could keep her between his chest and the bib of his overalls. Sometimes she catnapped behind the bib, only to pop up unexpectedly and yawn in the face of whomever might be talking with Red.

The addition of Dog to Aldous 'Red' Hensley's daily routine enriched not only his life but the local folklore as well. Red was a big man, with a frame like a mastodon and the weight to match. The contrast between him and Dog was at best humorous but not something anyone would comment on in their presence since Red was known to have a temper to match his size and his blazing red hair.

It was early when I finished my morning coffee and went outside to attach the bucket to the Westendorf front-end loader on the tractor that sat beside the barn. The air was cool, but as the sun rose above the tree-tops it hinted at the unrelenting heat. As much as it irritated me to admit it, I wanted to have the houses cleaned out before Wayne Staley darkened our door again. I was about to get on the tractor when Red's rebuilt 1964 Ford truck bumped and rolled up our driveway to the barn.

"Mornin', Red," I said. "You're out early; going to town?"

"Nope," he said, picking the spit cup off the dash and emptying a mouthful of tobacco juice before continuing. "I was wonderin' if you'd take a ride with me and Dog up the road a bit. There's something I think you should see. Maybe you ought to bring that new camera you been totin' around."

He looked me in the eye and then out the front window of his pickup and over to my fourteen ton feed bins. "Comin'?"

I wondered what the mystery was so I didn't mention that I was busy trying to get my houses cleaned out. Instead I said, "Okay, let me grab the camera."

I retrieved my new digital camera from the wall-mounted coat rack inside the kitchen door. I wasn't sure what I had hoped to do with it but I had started taking pictures of things that weren't going right in the chicken business. Pictures of birds that had run out of feed; pictures of cross-beaked, black-feathered or three-legged chickens; pictures of the powdered formaldehyde that they made us burn between batches; pictures of the unmarked chemicals sans instructions that they delivered for us to use; pictures of things that didn't belong in the feed bins, like the time red hydraulic fluid oozed out of the bottom. I never did get an explanation for that, but I did get a picture.

It was the summer of my discontent and now Red had intrigued me. I climbed into the passenger side of his truck and asked, "What's goin' on?"

As we turned left from the driveway onto the country road, Red told me what he saw the night before.

"I got up to get a drink of water 'cause Dog woke me. I keep a little stool by the window in the living room. She gets up on it and looks out if she hears something. It's usually squirrels or birds. They drive her crazy, but she just barks a little and then ignores them." He picked up the spit cup again, while fencing tools, snuff cans and work gloves vibrated on the dash. We stopped around a bend where no farmhouses were in view, across from the gate to his hay field. Dog peeked out of the side of his bib overalls, hopped out and walked across the bench seat to sniff my hand.

"After I got my drink, I went into the livin' room to see what got her riled up. That's when I saw two sets of lights through the trees at the far end of my hay field. One of them looked like a big rig. Well, since I only planned to cut hay once this year, I put my bred heifers in that field after it got about four inches of top on it. I still got them old wooden catch pens in the corner so I was afraid someone might be tryin' to rustle them heifers."

"Red," I said, "you should have called me or Dan. You shouldn't be going out there by yourself if there might be trouble. Those guys that rustle cattle wouldn't have any trouble putting a bullet in you to keep you quiet."

"Well, I wurnt sure, coulda been a midnight feed delivery truck broke down. You know how they come around any hour of the night to them broiler houses. Anyhow," he waved me off, "I couldn't go back to sleep 'til I knew for sure they ain't tryin to get my heifers."

"So I took the insurance piece," he said referring to a sawed off twelve gauge he kept in the closet, "got in the truck and drove down there. Before I could get up close, both them trucks took off like a bat out of hell in opposite directions. The big one passed me. The license plate was covered with mud and I couldn't read the truck numbers for all the glare, but it was a PU truck. I can tell you that much."

"And, the other truck?"

"Just a pickup, I couldn't tell nuthin' about it and at that point I wurnt about to go to chasing it. Couldn't even tell you if there was more than one person. I got out to check the lock on my gate and that's when I walked through all the feed."

Red put the truck in gear and pulled across the grassy culvert near the gate into where he was keeping his heifers. We got out walked back to the road.

"See here," Red pointed to huge piles of broiler feed on the side of the road and a thick spread of feed mixed with dirt and debris out in the lane.

"What in the world," I said as I walked across the road and clicked a couple pictures of Red by the piles. Then I took close up shots showing the size of the pellets and a patch of tire track from a heavy rig.

Red walked around to the back of the truck and pulled out several five gallon feed buckets and threw me a shovel and took one for himself. "We're gonna rattle some cages," he said as he scooped shovel after shovel of grain into the buckets.

I joined in and soon we had picked up the relatively clean feed and filled half a dozen buckets. The rest would be ground into the dirt or washed away if we ever got rain.

Red looked across the fields and I could feel the vibes of anger coming off of him, a certain portend of things to come.

"How many times," he asked, "you been a top grower and then for no good reason you're on the bottom of the heap, even though you're doing everything the same?"

"Well, Red, I guess that's happened to all of us, hasn't it? There are probably too many variables for us to ever know why we can't nail it every time."

"There's that and then there's the lyin', cheatin' and stealin' that's going on. It don't make much sense for them to be payin' us on competin' against our neighbor when they're stackin' the deck. Conversion rates, bullshit. It's window dressing. We won't never get to see how they figure it. We're just supposed to go on faith? Trust and believe in Jesus? Humph. Well Staley and Bible thumpin' Witherwax can kiss my ass; they're gonna hear about this."

"What do you mean? What do you figure is going on here?"

"That feed driver that's been deliverin' to us the last year or so told me a story once about some of them drivers; where if a man will leave a hundred dollars in the ticket box, he gets extra feed delivered that don't show on his ticket. I didn't pay him no mind at the time but now I think he was talkin' about hisself."

"You're saying someone in our complex is paying for extra feed and they're getting it out of our allotments?"

"Yep, that's what I think. I think he was making the dump into the pickup bed of the fella who's payin' him. I guess I should have followed the pickup but I didn't see the feed on the ground and I was still thinkin' about my heifers."

"So, I guess you didn't recognize the truck?"

"Naw, I was blinded by the headlights on the big truck and the pick-up was too far out of sight. You know we been talkin' about how to figure how much feed they bring. The company won't let us put scales in even if we have them certified. What does that tell you? The drivers know the company's cheatin' us so they probably figure it don't matter if they take a little too. Not that it's right but management filters down. Anyhow, it bothers me more that one of my neighbors might be doin' it, knowin' how it affects us."

That was more talking in one sitting than I usually got out of Red, so I continued to ply him with questions. "You got any ideas who might be paying him?"

"No," he paused. "I'd like to look at the ranking lists since we got that new driver last year. See if anybody's farm is always stayin' way on top."

"They may not even be from around here, Red."

"Yeah, I thought about that." He opened the door of the pickup, scooped Dog up off the seat and stuck her in the side of his overall top. She popped her head over the bib and peered through the steering wheel, her bristly head merging with Red's rust colored beard.

"What are you going to do?" I asked.

"I'm going to give Wayne Staley a piece of my mind about how he's running this chicken shit outfit. They got so damn much control over everything, they can damn well control their drivers."

The sun was higher now and piles of whipped potato clouds were in the southwest. The day was heating up and my shirt stuck to the vinyl seat back of Red's truck. It was going to be another scorcher but not near as hot as the conversation Red would have with Wayne Staley. I smiled and did nothing to discourage him.

Editor's Note: Excerpted from "Plucked and Burned" available on-line and at bookstores everywhere ISBN 0-9720293-2X

CHAPTER THIRTY-FOUR

So You Think You Would Like To Be in the Goat Business...

O r more specifically, the *meat* goat business. You have read all the literature about multi-species grazing, you've learned that goats will eat weeds and forbs and other nuisance greenery that your cattle don't care a bit about. You've read that goats can eliminate the need for costly chemicals as they take the place of hazardous herbicides. You learned that over 60,000 new legal immigrants enter our country each month, most of whom prefer "chevon". You've studied the advantages for a small family farm to be heavily diversified so that the ups and downs of various markets can balance each other out on the farm's bottom line. You figure you're farming full time anyway so what's one more creature on your already full slate of chores.

Well, overall that's a good reason to look into owning some goats. However, for every new addition to the family farm, there is some degree of learning curve. Depending on your past experience, the curve can be shallow or deep. There are some basic things to consider when deciding to go into the goat business so that you can be better prepared.

One of the familiar lines among goat ranchers is "if your fence can't hold water, it can't hold goats". Don't throw in the towel yet because, quite honestly, not too many farms have great fences. Practical and utilitarian is the key word here. Very likely you've got something like five strand barbed wire that's been in place since you helped your daddy put it up years ago or you just moved to the country and the old couple who sold you the place proudly announced that it has been cross fenced for fifty years. Such a fence will generally keep cattle in, notwithstanding a high libido bull and some amorous neighboring heifers, but goats will drift through it like smoke through the kitchen screen.

However, there are some simple solutions. You can successfully mount an offset "hot wire" that is connected to one of the modern New Zealand type chargers and keep your goats in the pasture where you intend for them to be. And for smaller areas, you might consider electric netting. An alternative is to run hog wire up against the existing barbed wire fencing. The downside to that approach is there will always be one goat in the bunch that thinks the pasture is greener on the other side and will insist on sticking its head through a hole only to get stuck. But, these are some of the fun things that you will learn to cope with when you tackle raising a herd of goats.

Let's say you've fixed your fence and now you want to buy some goats. If you've had previous livestock experience you will know that all too often folks dump their problems at the local sale barn. It is almost always a better deal to buy from a reputable breeder. You don't have to buy expensive, registered stock. You might find a dairy that is using a meat goat buck to freshen the does because they don't need to keep replacement does or because they are getting into the meat goat business as well.

Don't discount the idea of having some "milk goat" stock in your foundation does. A little bit of dairy blood - no more than half would be best – will insure a good milk supply in your mama goats. The milk breeds should provide good fertility. Feminine traits are inversely related to masculine traits like heavy muscling. As pretty as she is, a heavily muscled meat doe might not be the best choice if it turns out she doesn't milk well, doesn't breed every season and only has one kid each time. You can always put a heavily muscled sire over a less meaty but more fertile doe and get some great kids. As always, moderation and balance will serve you well.

At first your goal will be to obtain some good females that will raise nice heavy kids. Be sure to ask about the reproductive history of their dams. Did their mothers always have twins or triplets each breeding season? You may wish to buy these young does at weaning and raise them yourself. You'll get to know them individually, and more importantly, you'll be familiar with their health history. It is much easier to start out with healthy stock than to try and cure someone else's chronic problem, which in turn could end up affecting your entire herd. Be sure to quiz the seller about any health problems in their herd. Ask your vet what types of health problems affect goats in your area so you'll know the questions to ask.

A condition called "CL" or caseous lymphadenitis has been a controversial topic. It is caused by a bacterium that invades the lymph system. Some folks consider it only a cosmetic nuisance since the goat usually appears to be well and the resulting abscesses rarely affect the carcass. However, it is highly contagious and if you've never had goats on your place, you'd probably be wise to avoid it. It is said to stay in the soil for years and is relatively unaffected by extreme temperatures. It is endemic in the national goat population and you'll need to grill prospective sellers about it. A vaccine has been developed in New Zealand to protect against CL and can be purchased in Canada but unfortunately cannot be brought into the United States. Purportedly Colorado Serum is developing a vaccine that will be available in this country but at last report was some time off.

Before your does reach breeding age, which ideally will be anywhere from 9 to 12 months, you need to have selected a meat goat buck. Here it pays to buy the best buck you can afford. Kiko bucks are large framed, aggressive breeders and very hardy. If you plan to have a large operation with minimal individual attention, this is a breed to consider. Boer bucks, typically white with red heads, are generally showier, heavily muscled but usually not as aggressive in breeding. Since I've raised both breeds and admire them both, I will say that often the Boer is a more outstanding looking animal but the offspring is not as hardy as Kikos. I've found more of the Boer newborns need help and require bottling. Our Kiko mothers were so impressive that we coined the term that they had a "maternal edge".

There is a place for many breeds in the meat goat business. I would advise using them to your advantage, remembering the strengths of each. Some commercial meat goat producers are using a crossbred Kiko/Boer buck and finding it a rewarding combination. Some of our best kids were 75 % Kikos out of Kiko/Boer mothers. The Muslim market often prefers a solid white goat like the Kiko and that may be a consideration for your area. A large framed Spanish nanny can also be a fine addition to your herd of does. However, as cute as they may be, don't expect a miniature goat to raise a market size kid. You'll want good-sized females capable of weaning at least two big kids each.

There are many differences of opinion that are influenced by what breed people are selling. If you have an opportunity, talk to different commercial producers and get their input. The ultimate goal in meat goat production is to produce a forty-five pound kid, yielding a twenty-pound carcass, at roughly 100 days with no outside inputs. If the mother can raise a saleable product, then you have the potential to realize a profit.

This brings us to the point of how to realize a profit. At weaning you can sell the offspring to people who will take them directly to slaughter or you can sell to those who might be interested in feeding them out to a heavier weight. Some try this on pasture with supplements and others pen feed. Don't attempt this unless your pastures are an exceptionally healthy salad bowl mix with ample forage. You risk a post-weaning slump that will force you to supplement the kids with high dollar concentrates that defeat the reason for raising goats in the first place. My personal bias is to never resort to pen feeding goats. It is the avenue to ruin since you are required to supply purchased inputs. Not only the feed bill goes up but also the veterinary expense

It is imperative that you minimize purchased inputs. Small farms need to stay focused on the fact that energy from the sun is free and the little green chlorophyll factories in forage are capable of turning that energy into carbohydrate and protein to feed the animals. Our job is to wisely manage the use of our forage. Don't overstock your pastures. Just add a few goats at time so that there will be plenty of high quality forage available. Goats have the reputation of eating tin cans but actually their requirements are more demanding than cattle and they will pick the high protein leaves and grains from weeds and forbs. If there is enough forage, they will preferably graze above their shoulders much like deer. If they can do that, they not only select a good menu but they avoid parasite infestation. And, it will be kinder to your pocketbook.

Goats are much more susceptible to parasites than cattle and one of the biggest mistakes new producers make is thinking that more goats mean more profit. Actually unless you are very careful about your stocking rate, more goats can mean disaster. Anthelmintic (deworming) medicine is expensive and time consuming to administer. Also parasites can kill a goat quicker than the novice will notice. Be conservative with your stocking rate and you'll not have a problem. Goats are meant to forage, try to avoid raising them in pens. But do provide a safe shelter for them at night and during bad weather. If necessary, add guardian protection during the day. We used Anatolian Shepherd guardian dogs for our herd since the goat herd grazed heavily timbered, rocky terrain with constant predator pressure. You may have a situation that is somewhere between that and the pen method of raising goats.

Minerals are one input that will repay itself. Goats have higher needs for some minerals such as iodine and cobalt. We always kept a high quality loose mineral available, mixed with a little diatomaceous earth for parasite prevention. Don't forget that keeping your pastures healthy will also allow your animals to access minerals. Lime, unlike chemical fertilizers, will feed your soil in a way that increases soil microbes and other soil life that will in turn allow plants to access more minerals.

Most areas of the country have local markets now for goats but the infrastructure to market goats is still new and developing. You will have to research the opportunities in your area. Many farms have successfully sold to minority groups right off the farm for $1.00 per pound at weaning and up. Different ethnic groups favor carcasses of different ages. There is a great deal of information to be obtained by surfing the Internet. Many of the Universities provide up to date information on carcass research and ethnic holidays.

There are catalogs and books to help you with everything from supplies to how-to's. So read all you can. Remember to be a grass farmer first and that what works for someone else may not work for you. You will have to find your own way, one that is consistent with the philosophy of your farm. But, most of all, enjoy your goats. Watch them and let them teach you. They are curious creatures that will charm you from the beginning and make you wonder why you didn't have some sooner.

PART SIX

$\mathcal{A}$ Selection of Articles by Dr. Frank Pinkerton

aka "The Goat Man"

Editor's Note: Dr. Frank Pinkerton, aka The Goat Man, is a retired University extension goat specialist and industry consultant in meat goat management and marketing. He operated The Goat Works, a smallholder operation featuring Boer/Spanish crosses, primarily for the wether trade, from 1993 until late 2003 when the declining health of his wife necessitated its dispersal. Frank remains an active contributor to the industry with the generous sharing of his wide experience in various aspects of research and ranching. We are honored to have the following offering for the readers of The Meat Goats of Caston Creek.

(Below) Frank consulting.

(Right) Meat goats forage in the foothills of the Ouchita Mountains.

Frank walking his goat pasture in Grapevine, Texas.

CHAPTER THIRTY-FIVE

You Want To Do Meat Goats?

Since the late seventies, I have observed with professional concern, personal interest, and occasional alarm as owners and prospective owners considered expanding or initiating goat enterprises. Prior to reaching final decisions, some skillfully investigated, in-depth, the opportunities, constraints, and most probable cost-benefit ratios of various management and marketing alternatives; others, however, made only cursory investigations of enterprise options, the "fit" of their available resources, market availability/stability, etc. As might be expected, the success rate of such enterprise introductions and expansions was spotty indeed. In some states, disappointments, if not disasters, exceeded successes by considerable measure for several years (until bad experiences thinned out the losers and shared good experiences enabled improved success rates).

Among the most common failings exhibited, the tendency to start too big, or to get to big too fast, was paramount. This tendency was exacerbated when too little technical knowledge was teamed with inflated expectations and (too) short-term financing. A second common failing was to start the operation prematurely, i.e., to get the goats on-site *before*

sufficient fencing, facilities, supplemental feed, and predator/parasite control programs were in place. A third failing was to only belatedly realize that slaughter goat prices exhibit marked seasonal highs and lows and, furthermore, that marketing venues, transportation costs, shrinkage, and commission fees are also important cost considerations, not mere adjuncts to goat production. To some, a fourth difficulty was the surprising revelation that their friendly extension service person and Veterinarian who were ever so knowledgeable concerning local forage crops, beef cattle production, and animal health care didn't know shit about goat production, or even exhibit much interest in such exotic beasts. A corollary interpersonal problem sometimes occurred when good-intentioned goat-owning neighbors (with too little experience coupled with compensating motor mouths) were found, well after the fact, not to know shit, either.

For those *currently* contemplating the establishment or expansion of a meat goat enterprise, early recognition and detailed investigation of the several different types of operations to choose from would be most useful. Among the alternatives, each of which will require variable levels of financial commitments, different physical resources, and site-specific management schemes, are: smallholder/intensively managed herds; larger scale extensively managed herds; small, elite purebred seed stock herds, large purebred "expander" herds; specialized herds for the production of Youth Show wethers; herds held primarily for control of brushy/weedy lands or vegetation management of forest under-story, fire lanes, power lines, and water impoundments; and hobby herds subsidized for lifestyle enjoyment. Only after the final choice among types of enterprise has been made can one logically take further, specific actions, as described below.

Procurement of foundation stock
Selection of animals

Rational procurement of initial stock to implement the chosen type of enterprise requires that the owner first select a *breed* of meat goat and, thereafter, select individual animals within that breed. The *breed* chosen may be purebreds or "grades" (crossbreds). Readers should recognize that opinions regarding the one "correct" breed of goat for a given need vary quite widely (mathematically speaking, this may be put as: the number of such opinions is equal to the number of the discussants (squared) multiplied by the number of breeds known to the discussants). In point of fact, too little reliable data is available to enable analytically precise cost-benefit comparisons between breeds and their various crosses; live with it. On the other hand, some consideration should probably be given to the relative numbers of certain breeds and their most numerous crosses as to production locales and market venues.

Having arbitrarily but realistically guessed at the best breed for the enterprise, owners then must select individuals with attention to age/sex requirements of the initial herd. Selection of individuals is a rather imprecise undertaking at best. The basic assumption involved in visual selection is that there exists a *reasonably close relationship* between the *physical appearance* (phenotype) of an animal and its *actual performance* (genotype, as measured by its physiological functions of maintenance, growth, reproduction, lactation, and fattening as expressed in its responses to various physical environments). There is a further assumption, namely, that the selector *knows* (via training and/or experience) these imperfect relationships at least well enough to beat a random gate-cut procedure. Some do, some do not. In any case, the inexperienced are urged to obtain experienced help in choosing foundation animals; if errors still occur (as they surely will), blame may be conveniently placed.

As I have told many times in many places, evaluating/selecting the most desirable goat is rather like assessing pornography—it is fairly easy to do, but it is pure hell to describe. For instance, blemishes, health status, desirable structural traits, size/age ratios, body condition scores, and breed characteristics are relatively easier to evaluate/describe than are body conformation scores and (prospective) carcass grades. Reproductive efficiency/potential (fertility rate, milk production, mothering ability, longevity) is very difficult to visually assess, while trying to look for evidences of high feed conversion efficiency, daily feed intake, and rate of gain is an exercise in futility.

Pricing of foundation animals

Purchasing foundation meat goats typically involves considerable, perhaps faith-based confidence in one's capability to recognize a really good deal. Over the years, I have seen good deals and bad deals and some deals not easily categorized. The confluence of money or easy credit, buyer ignorance about goats/management/marketing with goat sellers (or traders) deeply steeped in the principles of free enterprise and unfettered by any real notions of observing the Golden Rule, can, and often does, result in serious financial disadvantage to novice buyers. As always, there is some lag time between the transaction and the dawning realization (as suspicion turns to certainty) that the deals were nowhere as good as the buyers previously thought. And, since most gullible buyers are loath to ever admit to themselves their documented poor judgment and demonstrated inept bartering skills, their common reaction is to place the blame solely on the seller. In such instances, shrewd sellers may, often with ill-concealed amusement, righteously point out that there really is no such thing as a correct/right price for a goat; *caveat emptor, friend.*

It follows, then, that the price of a goat in the real world is whatever the two parties agree to, then and there; nothing else counts. Those thinking otherwise are both gullible and vulnerable; accordingly, they are near certain to suffer the consequences of their shortcomings—usually sooner than later. In a rational, economically equitable goat world, buyers of foundation stock would logically expect to pay prices rather closely related to the (most likely) prices/returns to be received from the sale of subsequent off-spring. Unfortunately, such expectations are too often not realized, largely because inexperienced buyers are no match for veteran sellers possessing a gift for believable hyperbole, particularly concerning pretty, fat goats of "outstanding quality", all priced right, of course.

My own estimate of a fair price for a young (yearling or two year old), non-pregnant foundation-quality animal is one that should not exceed the current or likely sales value of two 50 lb market wethers (selection grade 2). To illustrate, such animals are currently selling for $1.10/lb; therefore, $110 would be the *maximum* price to be offered for the foundation doe. Readers should be keenly aware that such a doe might, in five years or so, have an (estimated) salvage value of only $50 and thus engender a lifetime depreciation loss of $60 (110-50=60). This $60, plus $44 to cover interest charges ($110 @ 8% x 5 yrs) totals $104 which must be spread over her five year saleable kid crop of, say, eight kids—a charge of $13/kid. Assuming the doe's maintenance costs (feed, health, breeding fees, repairs, fuel, etc.) to total $40/annum, brings the annual cost to $53/doe (13+40). If she sold 1.6 kids weighing 50 lbs each (net, after shrinkage) for a $1.10/lb (net, after marketing expenses), her annual gross would be $88 (80 lbs x 1.10) and her net would be $35 (88-53) for the year. This sobering, yet realistic net annual earnings figure per doe is certainly reason enough to warn against overpaying for foundation females.

Similar calculations should be applied to prospective herd sires whose estimated cost-benefit ratio must include charges for depreciation, interest on purchase cost, and annual maintenance. This total, divided by the number of does bred during his tenure, will yield a figure to be included in the annual maintenance charge for each doe. For commercial slaughter kid production, this figure simply must be kept well below $3/doe. For those enterprises selling animals at well above slaughter prices (for breeding stock or wether goat projects), relatively higher prices for bucks can be justified (as also for does, of course).

As a broker and smallholder producer, I sold during the last decade well over 2,000 female meat goats as well as small numbers of intact male kids, yearlings, and adults. Over 90% of the females I sold were doelings (mostly Spanish and Boer/Spanish crosses 4 to 10 months of age). They went to buyers who did not wish to pay the relatively higher prices prevailing for young does (as described above). Establishing/expanding a commercial herd with doelings can be something of a gamble...they may prove to be undersized at breeding age (7-10 months); some may be prematurely pregnant; some may have dysfunctional mammary anatomy; some may be late breeders; some may never breed; and those that do breed will have a lower incidence of twining. Given these caveats, I, along with others, priced such goats at a variable premium over the going San Angelo, TX auction price for *slaughter* kids of approximately the same age/weight/condition. Such premiums ranged $5-12/head depending on prevailing price levels, quantity taken, and, of course, my perception of individual buyer's interest—and knowledge. Insofar as I know, no customer ever came to lasting harm from these transactions; indeed, some became repeat buyers and/or provided referrals or recommendations.

For those contemplating the purchase of *purebred* foundation females, I strongly suggest that you should pay no more than the expected downstream selling price of two breeding-quality, weaned doelings. To do so, except in unusual situations, would almost guarantee pain and recrimination. Note that the economically rational maximum price to be paid for a *purebred buck* is much more difficult to estimate because of its' unpredictable salvage or resale value, but, in any case, the cost-accounting procedure is exactly the same (and so, too, is the chance for pain and suffering).

Those contemplating entry into the purebred goat business are urged to proceed very cautiously indeed. Relatively deep pockets are required to get in; an understanding and well-employed spouse is required to stay in. And, should you buy in at overly inflated prices, it might well require divine intervention for you to ever make a profit (or even to manage a quick, only modestly disastrous exit).

Sourcing foundation goats

Having made the required leap of faith *to do goats* and then having decided: 1) the kind of enterprise. 2) its initial scale, 3) level of investment, 4) breed, 5) purebred or grade, 6) numbers/ages/sexes, it is now time to buy goats (but *only* if facilities/fences/predator controllers/etc. are *actually* ready). Note that this is no time for unilateral decision-making; do include your spouse by all means—the average modern marriage is unlikely to survive an acrimonious goat controversy. Moreover, you should give early notice to your neighbors regarding the imminent arrival of goats at their boundaries, and also allay their fears of transmissible diseases, fence-crawling, overgrazing, water pollution, excessive noise, exotic odors, and overt sex; doing so *may* help you avoid abrupt loss of personal reputation and possibly social standing.

When should you buy goats?

Historically, the supply/availability of desirable, saleable goats of various ages, sizes, sexes, and reproductive status varies across years, seasons, and locations. Accordingly, there seems be no economically optimum time to purchase foundation goats (except perhaps during those instances in which environmental conditions in a given area force large scale selling—and concomitant lower prices to bargain buyers). On the other hand, individual buyers usually have rather particular needs regarding numbers, ages, mating/kidding times to meet seasonal marketing targets, site-specific feeding programs, stocking rates, etc. Consequently, resolution of this recurring supply/demand dilemma is, as earlier described, dependent on two-party price negotiations.

Where should you buy goats?

If possible, you should purchase goats as close to your location as possible. This not only reduces transportation costs and hauling stress, it also lets you take advantage of any earlier environmental acclimation to your area; moreover, it might well be good "p.r." for both players. However, if you determine that your precise needs and acceptable prices cannot be obtained locally, you have no choice but to look further afield. Spanish-type goats and their various crosses are concentrated in the Texas Hill Country (nearly a million head, currently), but there are others, usually in smaller herds, in the southeast and border states. Purebred Boer goats and Kiko goats are now at scattered locations in these same states and, increasingly, in the mid-Atlantic and northeast as also on the west coast.

There are a number of ways to identify possible sources of foundation stock, among them: commercial monthly publications, breed magazines, state and regional Goat Association newsletters, University agricultural extension offices, State Departments of Agriculture, Internet Websites, and, as always, interconnected producer referrals.

Who do you buy goats from?

This is a question even more difficult than: what is an equitable price? Goats may be purchased from: public auctions, private auctions (individual or group consignments), traders/brokers/order buyers, or ranchers and farmers. In my long experience as player/observer, buying directly from goat owners of *decent reputation* has proven to be the least painful for most purchasers. Livestock owners in general and many goat owners in particular know from first-hand, sometimes evil experience, that public auctions are places to sell, not to buy. The probability of getting decent quality, healthy goats at such venues is not great, although their prices will likely be comparatively lower than at private treaty sales. Buying through intermediaries (brokers, etc.) can be—indeed, often is—an uncertain, sometimes painful, exercise, the major difficulties being the source, health, and quality of goats being offered. In any case, you are dead certain to pay a premium over farm-gate prices (as earlier described in the section on pricing).

My first choice is to go to ranchers from whom I have bought goats previously or, secondly, to go to ranchers of well-known, reputable standing or, thirdly, if I am unable to get away, I recommend to the prospective buyer an order-buyer of proven capability and demonstrated integrity. Normally, I select my own purchases on-site and always from an excess of offerings; that way I can cull those that don't suit me and, if my selections don't suit me or my client, I have only myself to blame (as does my client). For those of you lacking in goat buying experience, I strongly urge you to make use of an advisor…consultant, order-buyer, successful goat producer, whatever.

It is, of course, *possible* that, as a greenhorn buyer, you could locate a descent set of goats at an equitable price by yourself. It is not, however, very *probable*—i.e., the odds are distinctly not in your favor. You simply can not logically expect that most sellers of goats would have your interest foremost in their minds during the negotiations. Goat owners are neither more nor less notable for their charitable treatment of unsuspecting buyers than are any other livestock owners. Indeed, any tendencies toward eleemosynary endeavors in general may be strongly resisted, except perhaps at Christmas or on the Sabbath. (Even then, the IRS is extremely suspicious that reported deductions often exceed actual contributions by an astonishing multiple). So...cuidado, hombre, y vaya con Dios (be careful, man, and go with God...whom you may come to sorely need, as also a sympathetic and patient banker, should you elect to sally forth without benefit of more worldly counsel).

How do you get your new goats home?

Having selected your goats, paid your tab, and had a celebratory handshake, it is now time to load-out. Loading goats, particularly from rather rustic facilities, can be a bit more thrilling than you might suppose; coarse language, agility, and perseverance are usually required in good measure. Contrarily, hauling goats is not a particular problem *if* your unit will hold convicts or water. More precisely, side boards need to be not less than 54 inches high on open trailers and pickups. Concerning required floor spacing, we have successfully used 1.25 square feet/goat for weanlings, 1.5 ft for 50/60 pounders, 1.75 for 80/90 pounders, and 2.0 for larger goats. Commercial haulers commonly pack them tighter, saying that the goats haul better (it also reduces hauling cost/head/mile, but *only* if the goats are all alive and reasonably well on arrival; this may not be the case.)

Hauling costs/head vary widely depending on distance, carrier size, owner/driver, etc. Currently, commercial "pots" can move goats at about $2.25/*loaded* mile; double-deck gooseneck rigs (150/250 head) may be had for $1.60 or so per loaded mile. Driving your own pickup/trailer for *smaller* loads may easily engender costs in excess of a $1.00/loaded mile (actual out-of-pocket trip expenses will be less, of course, but, you can not ignore depreciation, repairs, etc. forever).

How far or long can you haul goats without off-loading? Slaughter goats are commonly hauled from San Angelo, TX to the NJ/PA area nonstop...18/1900 miles in 36-40 hours. The stress on such goats is high and a small percentage may die. The usual shrinkage is 3-4% (5-6 % if calculated on the original farm weight). More often than not, most were not properly handled prior to loading.

You can reduce stress on keeper goats by reducing floor density, by watering and feeding them 2-3 hours prior to loading, by driving carefully, and staying on interstates insofar as possible. If you are taking more than 24 hours, an 8 hour rest stop would be beneficial, but it might not be physically possible or economically feasible. The hassle of off-loading/reloading is also stressful. Lengthy rest stops without off-loading are negative in effect and not recommended.

In any case, when you get the goats home, put them into an isolated, grassed paddock with adequate watering space; offer hay if needed, but no grain; provide shelter only if weather conditions warrant. Thereafter, observe them closely for the next few days, removing any "suspicious" individuals for appropriate action. Note that it may take several days for respiratory and other problems to surface. There is some controversy regarding use of various antibiotics just prior to shipment or shortly after arrival. I don't, but others do so, even while conceding that the extra hassle during treatment may be detrimental. Sometimes goats show diarrhea on or shortly after arrival. This is more likely to be a reaction to stress than a gastrointestinal "bug" of some sort. Clean water, adequate nutrition, and elapsed time will frequently see a quick return to proper goat pills. On the other hand, treatment may sometimes be necessary; either way, such quandaries add to one's experience.

Editor's Note: Following his retirement in 1993 from a forty year University career encompassing teaching, extension, research, administration, and international work in animal science with the last fifteen years focusing on goats for milk, fiber, and meat, Dr. Frank Pinkerton established a small-holder meat goat enterprise in eastern Texas, primarily for the production of Youth Show wethers and commercial breeding females. He also undertook private, USDA, and University consultant assignments in management and marketing of meat goats. In 1994/5, while on a consultancy to the Rural Economic Development Center/Mid-Carolina Council of Governments, he edited, and contributed to, the creation of a Handbook on meat goat production and marketing. Among his several contributions was one concerning the procurement of foundation stock for initiating or expanding meat goat enterprises. It was a relevant topic then—and would seem especially so now, given

the current, documented need to increase the national supply of goats to meet rapidly expanding consumer demand. The foregoing is an updated, expanded version of the original to reflect current challenges and opportunities for meat goat owners.

CHAPTER THIRTY-SIX

Forage-Based Feeding Programs for Meat Goats

Preface

I t has been my good fortune over the years to have observed an exceptional variety of feeding programs used by owners engaged in various types of meat goat operations at many domestic locations and several international venues. But, no matter their scale or scope or location, certain commonalities were always and everywhere evident. All depended upon the use of forage-based feeding programs of one sort or another. Furthermore, nearly all were in agreement that, only when deficiencies in either forage quantity or forage quality threatened acceptable productivity levels, was it economical (cost-beneficial) to provide supplemental feeds to their herds. It was during these years that I came to understand that fat goats could be indicative of sub-optimum grazing management and, secondly, that excessively fat goats could be a health menace—to themselves and to cash flow statements. It is the purpose of this paper to provide certain insights concerning the principles of forage-based goat management.

Introduction

Long farm-level experience demonstrates that *commercial* meat goats must get a high percentage of their required daily nutrients from forages if the enterprise is to be economically viable. Exceptions to this sweeping statement occur only in those instances in which the nutrient value of the annual forage off-take is less than the combined (amortized) cost of owning the land and the variable (operational) costs of producing the usable forage.

All goats, no matter their breed, size, age, or sex, require the same basic nutrients, but in varying amounts. These are: protein, "energy", minerals, vitamins, and water. The daily intake (ration) of an individual goat must contain adequate protein from the diet being consumed because no other dietary nutrient can be substitutedsubstitute for it. Contrarily, the goat's daily energy need may be derived from a mixture of dietary carbohydrates (sugars, starches, cellulose, hemi-celluloseand fiber) or from dietary fat, or even from excess protein in the diet. A goat probably requires some minimum quantity of dietary fat, but the percent is not precisely known.

Nutrients from feedstuffs are required by a goat for *body maintenance* (basal metabolism and physical activity) and for *physiological functions* (growth, gestation, lactation, and fat deposition) The daily maintenance requirements may range from 50 to 100% of total daily nutrient requirements, depending on whether the goat is also engaged in one or more physiological functions.

Nutrient Requirements of Goats

The initial, official compilation of nutrient requirements of goats was published in 1981 by the National Research Council, Washington, D.C. Since then considerable research to improve the scope and the precision of these recommendations has been conducted. A comprehensive review and summation of these domestic/international research findings, under the leadership of Langston University, Langston, OK has recently been completed. It is expected that the resulting updated, official NRC recommendations will be available in 2005. In the interim, sufficient producer experiences and University findings provide useful information for the practical, reasonably accurate feeding guidelines used in this paper.

Sylvia Tomlinson

Basic nutritional principles for utilizing forage-based feeding programs

Daily feed intake of goats ranges from 3 to 4 percent (occasionally more) of their body weight as expressed in pounds of *dry matter*/head/day. Dry matter content in pasture forages ranges widely (12-35%) depending on plant species, plant maturity, season, and rainfall, while the dry matter content of hays and concentrate feeds ranges 86-92%. *Actual daily feed intake in pounds/head/day* is influenced by body weight, the % of dry matter in the feeds eaten, palatability, and physical environment of the animal, and, in particular, its *physiological functions* of growing, gestating, lactating, fattening. To illustrate, a non-lactating/non-pregnant yearling doe weighing 100 lbs might consume about 3 lbs of dry matter/day (3.0%) from pasture grasses, but if she weighed the same and were lactating (and thus needing more nutrients), she would likely consume around 4 lbs of dry matter/day (4.0%). (If the pasture grasses being consumed contained, say, 25% dry matter, the doe would actually be eating 12-16 lbs of green forage/day in these illustrations).

The total quantity of protein needed/day by a goat is the sum of protein needed for maintenance (dependent on body weight) plus all the protein needed for its particular physiological functions. A rapidly growing kid (30-50 lbs, male or female) seems to require from 12-14% protein in its daily intake of dry matter, while a lactating doe weighing 120-160 lbs may require 14-16% protein (dry matter basis). Non-lactating does require less % protein in their daily dry matter intake than (third trimester) gestating does do; both require about 20-25% less than lactating does of comparable weights. Readers should be aware that too little dietary protein will cause reduced performance of physiological functions. Contrarily, protein in excess of the goat's metabolic needs will neither hurt the animal nor appreciably improve its performance. Excess daily protein intake typically occurs when goats are on lush pasture or being improperly fed (offered excessive supplemental protein, usually in the winter) but...not to worry.

The quantity of energy needed/day by a goat is, like protein, the total of that needed for maintenance plus the aggregate amount that is needed for all physiological functions. As indicated earlier, this daily energy can be generated (derived) from the digestion of a variety of carbohydrate sources as also from dietary fat and excess dietary protein. The quantity

177

of energy needed for daily maintenance purposes is body-weight depend-ent, and this energy expenditure has *priority demand over physiological functions*. If an immature goat has insufficient energy intake per day beyond that needed for maintenance, its rate of growth will be depressed. If a young, non-pregnant doe has only enough energy intake/day for maintenance plus normal growth, she may not conceive or, if she does conceive, she may abort in the third trimester. A post-partum doe lacking sufficient energy for lactation will lose weight rapidly (by depleting body fat) and, thereafter, milk less per day and for limitedfewer days; conse-quently, her offspring will demonstrate poor growth rates, or even starve.

The specific requirements for minerals and vitamins needed by goats for both maintenance and physiological functions are not precisely known, but certainly goats do have minimum daily needs for these various nutri-ents. If the forages (or other feedstuffs) being eaten do not furnish ade-quate amounts of minerals and *fat-soluble* vitamins (ADEK), they must be added to the diet in order to support proper animal performance (if oth-erwise adequately fed, the rumen flora of a goat will manufacture suffi-cient *water-soluble* vitamins to meet basic needs; thus, such supplementation is only rarely needed).

The quantities of water needed daily for goat maintenance and for physi-ological functions are not known. Common sense suggests that, whatever the total for these needs, there are additional factors affecting water intake...diurnal temperatures, relative humidity, adequacy of shade or windbreak or cover, and distance to and frequency of watering. In any case, insufficient water intake will depress goat performance earlier, and more severely, than any other dietary insufficiency; accordingly, adequate water is thea paramount management concern. Caveat: decent water quality, not just quantity, is a must—if you can't drink it, don't offer it to your goats either.

Basic principles of forage management for optimum utilization by goats

With rarest exception, warm season pastures used for goats are com-posed of multiple species of grasses. These grasses may be perennial or annual, and they often have accretions of other plant species (browse, weeds, forbs, legumes, and, seasonally, small grains and cool season grasses). All these species contain varying quantities of protein and energy plus minerals and vitamins that are useful for goats. Although goats seem to prefer browse to grasses by some margin, they will do very well on pastures without browse or weeds. Because goats are particularly adept at selecting the most nutritious plants (and, within plants, the most nutritious portions) from mixed plant populations, they often do reasonably well on grazing areas considered by man and cow alike to be relatively low in quality *if the quantity available is sufficient.* Public perceptions to the contrary, goats can not in fact economically turn poor quality vegetative matter into meat and milk. Successful managers know this; novices may not last long enough to discover it.

The economic return to be gained from grazing pastures with goats depends on the *yield* of dry matter/acre and on the *quality* of the forages eaten. Basic factors affecting annual forage yield and quality are: plant specie, plant health, soil fertility, soil moisture, and soil temperature. Yield/acre and forage quality can also be appreciably influenced by grazing management decisions. Indeed, this variable yield and quality response-capability is the scientific basis for maximizing goat off-take (and profit/acre or head) from pastures.

Note that the physiologically-determined growth patterns of pasture plants make it impossible to simultaneously manage pastures for maximum yield of dry matter/acre and for highest quality because yield/acre *increases* with maturation of plants while quality *decreases* as plants mature (contain less protein and more indigestible fiber). Given this dilemma, optimum pasture management requires *on-going compromise* to achieve acceptable forage yield/quality across the growing season.

This required management compromise is achieved by controlling the *intensity and the frequency of forage plant defoliation.* Grazing intensity refers to the degree of plant defoliation (residual stubble height), while grazing frequency refers to the number of defoliations over time. Newly defoliated plants subsequently seek to recover, thus adding some weight (yield) while also producing higher quality tissue (higher protein, lower fiber). These serial defoliations, sometimes referred to as managing for maximum leafiness, are most efficiently achieved by employing a management system called rotational grazing.

Rotational grazing by goats is best accomplished by dividing (fencing) the farm or ranch into some number of smaller pastures and thereafter controlling goat movement to/from these lesser units across time. *Stocking density* refers to the number of goats per pasture and is usually expressed as number of mature goats/acre. Stocking densities may be adjusted to reflect herd characteristics (age, size, lactation status, etc.), but, in any case, for a given pasture size, the greater the stocking density, the shorter the grazing duration required to defoliate the forage down to the proper stubble height (which varies by major types of plants being grazed).

For *extensively* managed rotation schemes (usually larger acreages, more arid environments, with many species of browse plants), the stocking rate can vary widely; 2-5 acres/per mature goat are typical. The duration of grazing each pasture is primarily dependent on the grazing density chosen; six to 12 week periods are commonly used. The frequency (timing) of grazing pastures can be adjusted to "rest" them for various intervals so as to allow sufficient time for proper recovery of the forage plants. For *intensively* managed rotation schemes (usually found on relatively small operations in humid areas) stocking rates may *average* 2-3 mature goats/acre/grazing season. Grazing durations of 5-7 days may be used in conjunction with stocking rates ranging from 10 to50 goats/acre, sometimes more. Again, grazing frequencies should be chosen to promote the necessary regeneration of plant root reserves.

Using rotational grazing systems featuring higher densities and shorter durations has been shown to increase goat productivity/acre, as compared to *continuous* grazing, by some 12-20%, or more, depending on the particular grass/browse species involved. About 3/4s of such increases are thought due to improved forage quality with the remainder due to increased forage yield (and possibly to improved health care engendered by closer, more frequent animal observation).

As always, improvements in production efficiency (more goats/acre) engender added costs. Those considering rotational grazing practices, on large or small acreages, should recognize that fencing costs will be increased substantially when building multiple, smaller pastures/paddocks...more wire, posts, gates, lanes, watering devices, labor, and, if needed, shelters). Similarly, fertilizing pastures may, or may not, be cost effective depending on soil/plant needs, rainfall, stocking rates, goat prices, etc. Initial, high rates of fertilizer applications can, and should, be reduced over time as nutrient recycling from the goat manure will provide needed soil nutrients. One must always calculate the likely cost-benefit ratios when assessing management alternatives.

Supplemental feeding of goats on pasture

The primary factor affecting plant quality (nutrient composition) of warm and cool season forage of whatever species is age of plant. As plants mature, their protein content decreases, and their *indigestible fiber content increases* (lower cellulose, higher lignin); thus overall plant digestibility is reduced. For warm season pasture grasses in particular, forage quality and (re)growth rates begin to decline appreciably by fall equinox (or earlier, if rainfall is limiting). Subsequently, the quantities of plant nutrients available to the goat will become, over time, insufficient to meet some, perhaps all, of its daily nutritional needs. A goat consuming inadequate protein, energy, or minerals can draw from its body reserves of these nutrients (lose weight) without adverse effects on performance, but only for a relatively short time. In any case, going into the winter is no time for a goat to be in negative nutritional balance of any sort.

In theory, an owner could calculate mathematically the percentage of protein and digestible nutrients needed in the forage to meet the requirements for a particular set of goats being pastured. He could also take representative samples of the available forage and obtain laboratory analyses (in percentages). If the two sets of figures "matched', and if the quantity of forage available were adequate, no supplementation would be needed—-at that point in time. If, however, the protein and/or energy content of the forage was lower than the goat's needs, or if the quantity of forage available was judged (guessed) to be insufficient, supplementation would be necessary—-and, usually, it would be economical to do so. Readers should know that such calculation/testing is only rarely done; instead, owners rely on observation, experience, and advice—and hope for the best.

As long as quantities of fall forage remain adequate, dietary deficiencies of protein are likely to occur well before energy deficiencies do. In such cases, sufficient supplemental protein should be offered in some form, either daily or every second day. As always, there are multiple choices as to chemical composition, physical form, palatability, and price of available products. (Remember also that any feedstuff, or mixture of feeds, used to provide protein will also provide a considerable quantity of energy).

Generally speaking, one should choose the product that has the lowest *price/lb of protein*; to do so, divide the price/hundredweight of feed by the pounds of protein in the sack…e.g., 20 % CP on the feed tag means 20lbs protein/cwt. The price/lb of the feed is of lesser importance to owners of goats than to sellers of feed; similarly, the quality of protein (its amino acid content) is more important to the feed seller than to the goat whose rumen flora can convert lower quality, *lower priced* proteins into higher quality amino acids.

Experienced owners also are aware of the need to seriously consider additional factors when choosing among prospective supplements, e.g., relative palatability, potential for wastage, feeding equipment on hand or needed, and ease of handling/storage. And, not least, does the physical form of the feed (and available trough/rack space) allow a reasonable chance for fairly equitable intakes among competing goats whose unwillingness to share is notorious? If not, uneven, and uneconomical, performance will soon become evident. Many seemingly poor-doing goats may simply lack in aggressive feeding behavior; they may or may not warrant culling, depending on specific management priorities.

Over the years I have practiced several, and observed many, variations of supplementing needy goats during the winter. Grazing small grains is a nutritionally sound practice to supplement lower quality hays or deferred, standing pasture. Only 2-3 hours grazing per day, at a stocking rate of 10-15 mature goats acre, can provide adequate protein and energy supplementation (while also limiting forage loss due to trampling). Such pastures are particularly responsive to intensive rotational grazing practices, but readers should be aware that the costs of establishing/using such annual forage crops can be comparatively high.

Some of us owners have deferred and subsequently grazed dry, relatively low quality warm-season grasses and browse in lieu of feeding hays of similar quality in order to avoid the sometimes high nutrient cost of hays and also the typically large nutrient losses that occur during feeding and storage. This may well be an economical feeding strategy, particularly so when high protein supplements are relatively cheap. A half pound of 41-44% protein oilseed cake/head/day will supply about .2 lb of protein (or about half of the daily requirement of a mature, gestating doe). Alternatively, a pound of 20% protein cubes/cake per head/day will also supply .2 lb of protein. In either case, the doe could get her remaining protein need from 3-4 lbs of low protein standing grass or hay.

Other owners prefer to winter goats on hay only. If the hay contains about 11-13% protein and at least 55% digestible nutrients (dry matter basis), it would adequately support gestating goats; lactating does would likely require additional protein from some source. Experienced goat feeders know all too well that hay availability, cost, and quality varies widely over time and place, and, to reiterate, costly waste is sure to occur during feeding and storage. Feeding high quality legume hays (16-20% protein) as the sole source of nutrients is particularly wasteful in that the protein intake will be excessive and expensive. As noted earlier, excessive protein is not harmful, just uneconomical…the surplus protein being converted to energy and to ammonia that is excreted in the urine. Since high protein feeds almost always cost more than high carbohydrate feeds, the phrase, pissing away one's money seems particularly apropos.

Still other owners, particularly those engaged in production of purebred and other special-purpose/higher value goats choose to feed 1.5 to 3.0 lbs of concentrate (grain mixture) testing 14 to 16% protein in addition to above-average quality hay *ad lib* during the winter. Such a strategy supplies extra energy as well as supplemental protein. Assuming the goats are healthy, it virtually guarantees excellent body condition; indeed, carried to excess, it will cause the deposition of considerable subcutaneous fat, thereby helping to mask certain of phenotypic sins. Admittedly, such a procedure is often quite cost-beneficial, especially for high-dollar Show animals.

A relatively few owners, particularly those managing small herds of special-purpose goats, borrow a page from dairy goat owners and feed their goats a "complete ration". As fed, year round, it is an "all in one" combination of feedstuffs containing adequate protein, energy, minerals, and fiber to meet the particular needs of this or that group of goats. Typically, it is a *customized* mixture containing 30 to 40% roughages (high fiber feeds, chopped or ground) and 60 to 70% grains/high protein meals) to be fed *ad lib* once or twice daily. Properly formulated (and pelleted to prevent sorting of ingredients), it will be nutritionally adequate and convenient to feed, but it will also be relatively expensive.

There are, of course, many additional ways to properly feed goats when "green" forage is unavailable. Indeed, it must sometime seem to novices that the number of ways equals the number of owners. This does not mean, of course, that all are both nutritionally sound and economically feasible. Caveat emptor, etc.

And now, a concluding word about mineral supplements for goats. Readers, particularly those being subjected to blandishment by mineral salesmen or enticingly worded advertisements in the farm press, should realize that precise, individual mineral needs for all classes of goats are, to date, far from being completely identified. Indeed, many of the existing University and commercial recommendations are based, in part, on extrapolations from sheep and dairy cattle data and, in part, on ranch/farm level "research" experiences (I use mix XYZ, it seems to work, ergo, it must be okay).

All forages (and other feedstuffs) contain some combination of minerals of which some, or all, *may* actually be required by goats. Laboratory analyses to identify minerals in any particular forage sample are available to owners at various costs. Only by knowing the mineral contents of the particular forage mixture and also knowing the precise mineral requirements of the grazing goats can one then accurately formulate a mixture of minerals to provide any missing dietary minerals; note that every time the class of goat changed or the forage composition changed, one would have to reformulate the mineral supplement. This being economically untenable, one necessarily resorts to purchasing one or more mineral mixtures (on the basis of external advice, price, or salesmanship or whatever) and then offering them *ad lib* to one's goats. Depending on palatability and accessibility, the goats may indeed eat enough, frequently enough, to satisfy their on-going needs (over-indulging is very seldom a nutritional problem though it can be uneconomical…careful here). But, in no case, should you become persuaded that goats can, and will, correctly choose, from among several single mineral supplements on offer, only those necessary to properly balance their needs.

CHAPTER THIRTY-SEVEN

Supplemental Winter Feeding of Goats

I n a companion piece in this section entitled, Forage-Based Feeding Programs For Meat Goats, I focused on a goat management scheme featuring maximum grazing with seasonal supplementation of protein, energy, and minerals as needed. The information presented below targets goat enterprises featuring shorter grazing seasons and, consequently, longer periods of feeding preserved forages which often require extended feeding of supplemental protein, energy, and minerals. Readers are asked to bear with unavoidable repetition and overlap as between these two updated presentations.

You are also asked to remember that goats evolved over time and place as forage-consuming animals, and for centuries they maintained and reproduced themselves on browse, forbs, "weeds", and pasturage without added grain, protein, or minerals. Doubtless mortality was high and productivity low, but...they did survive. Goat survival and goat enterprise survivability are not, however, mutually inclusive phenomena.

In the past few years, farm prices for goats have increased sharply and are, in mid 2005, at record highs. Better prices have encouraged many goat owners to strive for improved herd productivity through better management strategies and tactics. Gains in productivity may be made most rapidly by improvements in herd health care and nutritional status and, less rapidly, via improvements in herd genetics. Assuming a forage-based enterprise with adequate quantity and quality of forage for six to 9 months per year at tolerable cost, the best chance for further improving both herd performance and bottom-line economics would seem to be an astute winter supplemental feeding program.

Accordingly, owners need to know sufficient theory and practice to economically implement such a program. Overfeeding, underfeeding, improper dietary composition, and overpriced feeds/unit of nutritional value all increase feed costs per head, thereby decreasing net profit per enterprise. It is the purpose of this paper to identify certain opportunities and constraints to proper supplementation. As an aside, I have long noted that inherited wealth or an understanding and well-employed spouse are required to sustain goat-related cash flow deficits. If you have neither, I suggest you either heed this information or sell out in order to preserve domestic tranquility.

Nutrient Requirements of Meat Goats

All breeds (and crossbreds), sexes, and ages of goats require the same basic nutrients: protein, energy, minerals, vitamins, and water. The daily diet *must* contain adequate protein because no other dietary nutrient can substitute for it. Contrarily, energy needs may be met with dietary carbohydrates (starches and/or fiber) or fats or even excess protein. Nutrients are required by the goat for maintenance and productive functions (growth, gestation, lactation, and fattening).

Maintenance requirements are used for basal metabolism (maintain body temperature and support vital functions) and for physical activity. The daily maintenance requirements may range from 50 to 100% of total daily nutrient requirements, depending on whether the animal is also engaged in one or more productive functions. Maintenance requires relatively more energy than protein; contrarily, growth and pregnancy (particularly in the last trimester) require relatively more protein than energy. Lactation requires large quantities of both protein and energy, while fattening requires much "surplus" energy but little to no protein. Note that purposefully fattening a goat is uneconomical in two ways: first, it takes 2.25 times as much feed to put on a pound of body fat as it does to put on a pound of muscle (protein and water) and, secondly, the current commercial market discriminates heavily against overly fat goats. Muscular, well-conditioned goats are considered desirable while excessive internal or external body fat is a consumer no-no.

The daily needs of protein and energy for goats may be expressed in actual quantities of crude protein (pounds C.P.) and energy (pounds of total digestible nutrients—TDN) by adding up the amounts of each needed for maintenance, milk production, etc. Alternatively, daily protein and energy needs may be more conveniently expressed as percentages of the daily feed intake (*on a feed dry matter basis*). Note that goats will consume, on the average, 3.5/4.0% of their body weight in feed dry matter per day; the actual dry matter intake/day may range 3.0 to 4.5%, sometimes more, depending on many factors (e.g., body weight, % dry matter in the feed, palatability of the feed, nutritional needs for productive functions, environmental conditions, etc.). CAUTION: level of dry matter intake/day strongly influences the *calculated* % of protein or %TDN needed in the daily ration. For instance, if a 100 pound animal having a daily need for .4 pound of protein got it in 3.0 pounds of dry matter, the % protein would be 13.3; if she got the same .4 pound of protein in 4.0 pounds of dry matter, the % would be 10.0.

Using various research results and long-term producer feeding experiences, including my own, I have estimated protein and energy requirements for certain categories of goats (by body weight, sex, and reproductive status. Thereafter, I calculated the quantities and % of protein needed in a given supplement based on probable intake levels of hays containing various levels of protein. Readers should understand that my figures are only approximate; more accurate recommendations will be published in 2005 by the National Research Council, Washington, D.C. In the meantime, anyone telling you he possesses precise figures for goat nutritional requirements or for infallible feeding recommendation bears very close watching—he has already lied to you at least once.

The differences in protein and energy content of the supplements for these categories of goats, as described below, may seem rather small to you, but underfeeding can have measurable adverse consequences on goat performance. The uninformed may blame such sub-par performances on poor genetics or poor health for what are, in point of fact, poor feeding practices by the owner. Wise owners recognize that, contrary to popular belief, goats cannot create meat and/or milk out of unlimited, but poor-quality feedstuffs (low protein, high fiber). The merely ignorant can, with due diligence, expect to triumph over such misinformation; for those more mentally challenged, an early exit from goat ownership is quite likely, perhaps even desirable.

Feeding Practices

During the warm season grazing period, goats will very likely meet all their nutritional requirements from whatever combination of forages is available, assuming their quantity is not limited. In such situations, I usually provide only a trace mineralized salt and a phosphorus supplement such as Dical(cium phosphate) just to be on the safe side. (Forages are relatively higher in calcium than in phosphorus; grains are the opposite). During late summer/fall and on through the winter, standing forages decline sharply in quality and quantity. Thus, some quantities of supplemental protein and energy have to be supplied to maintain satisfactory performance.

If winter pastures of ryegrass or small grains (oats/wheat/barley) can be planted in early fall, they can usually be grazed by/before Thanksgiving and into May. Goats can harvest sufficient amounts of these forages to meet their nutritional needs while grazing only 2-3 hours/day. Because of the high water content of these forages, however, it may be beneficial to also offer a pound or so of non-legume (low protein) hay/head (adds dry matter and suppresses diarrhea).

Many successful goat owners have found that adequate winter rations may consist of dry standing grasses and/or non-legume hays (6-8% protein), plus a commercially available protein source. In eastern TX and the southeastern U.S., Coastal Bermudagrass, Bahiagrass, or Fescue hays fed *ad lib* plus 1 pound/head/day of 20% protein pellets/cubes will be adequate for pregnant does; lactating does *might* benefit from an additional quarter pound/head/day, depending on the protein level of the hays being used. If the hays used were in the 9-11% protein range, it would probably be possible to reduce the protein in the pellets to 16% or, alternatively, reduce the quantity of 20% protein pellets to 3/4 pound/head/day for pregnant does. Be reminded that, while overfeeding of protein is uneconomical, so also is underfeeding (because of reduced performance). I tend to err on the side of oversupply, but freely admit this may not be cost-beneficial.

In those cases where better quality hays are available at "reasonable" prices, I prefer to use them and thus avoid feeding either protein or energy supplements. Such hays (usually highly fertilized non-legume or mixed legume/non-legume) range 12-14% protein and have adequate digestibility (55-60% TDN); thus, they can normally support pregnant/lactating does. However, heavily milking does (with twin or triplets) would probably benefit from some corn, say, .5 to 1.0 pound/head/day, but again, the cost-benefit ratios realized might not be positive.

The use of high protein legume hays (16-20%) such as alfalfa or alfalfa/grass mixtures would be quite sufficient for any goat's nutritional needs, if fed *ad lib.* But, the historically higher prices for such hays simply make it uneconomical to feed them to goats as compared to other, cheaper hays. (Adding, as some do, a daily quantity of grain just exacerbates the problem, although the goats will do very well indeed). In those exceptional circumstances when the protein in high quality legume hays costs less than the protein in grain-based protein supplements, one could opt to feed legume hay every other day and lower protein/cheaper grass hay on alternative days so as to achieve adequate performance and economical feeding cost. *Do not feed both hays simultaneously because palatability/greed will result in inequitable protein intake/head/day.*

For kids 3-6 months of age, I use a pound or so of 15-16% protein feed plus grass hay; for older kids, including those in early pregnancy, I prefer a pound or so of 13-14% protein feed plus grass hay. For suckling kids, I have found a creep feed of 12-14% protein to be adequate IF milk flow is adequate; if not, *ad lib* feeding of a 15-16% protein mix is recommended. I concede these protein levels may well be a bit higher than really necessary, but maximizing growth rates can lead to earlier breeding of doelings and bloomier appearance of wethers and buck kids— probably this is cost-beneficial *most* of the time.

There can sometimes be a special need for added energy and, possibly, for protein supplementation for does about to be bred, no matter the season. If prevailing forages are inadequate in quality or quantity, one may offer supplemental feed beginning 21-30 days prior to breeding time and lasting for 14 days or so after the bucks are removed. This management tool is call *flushing,* and it is done to increase ovulation and conception rates of the exposed does. Flushing can be economically feasible only if the forage base is inadequate. Dietary energy is frequently more limiting than dietary protein in such situations. That being the case, offering .25

to .5 pound of shelled corn/head/day could supply sufficient energy (but not protein, corn having only 7-8% protein). To add protein, one could offer .25 to .5 pound of 20% protein pellets (which would also provide additional energy). The flushing period can last for 70-90 days and require 25-35 pounds of feed costing perhaps $.10/.13/pound, thus adding $3-5/hd to annual doe maintenance cost. One would likely need to achieve about a 10% increase in kids weaned/sold to break-even…quite doable, but not guaranteed. All depends on actual nutritional status of the does, with/without the supplement.

Logistics of Feeding

It is easy enough to talk about optimum supplemental feeding of goats, but the reality of doing so is sometimes more difficult than it might seem, particularly to the inexperienced goat handler. One of the better ways of managing actual feeding operations is to segregate the herd into smaller groups according to various characteristics, e.g., their age, sex, size, reproductive status, and, possibly, body condition. Such categories will have somewhat different nutritional needs and thus require variable quantities and/or compositions of supplements. In essence, one seeks to feed each set of goats separately, properly, and economically.

To do this requires separate areas, adequate troughs/racks, and feed mixtures of specific composition/form for the targeted groups. Such personalized attention obviously incurs added costs in terms of feed storage, facilities, and labor, but trying to do otherwise, i.e., a one-feed-fits-all goats approach is certain to lead to erratic intake, uneven goat performance, and, accordingly, to reduced herd off-take (fewer kids born, lesser survival rates, lighter weight kids weaned/marketed). Handling all goats as one group does reduce labor, but at what real cost? Even when you do form separate feeding groups, how do you manage them to "ensure" that individual goats get their fair share? It is not easy; indeed, one can only hope that variations in individual daily intake "average out" on a weekly basis.

Putting out hay daily in racks or bunks (or less satisfactorily, on more or less clean ground) is readily done, though sometimes sinfully wasteful, depending on physical design of the feeders. I have found 1 linear foot/goat to be quite sufficient space (if feeding hay *ad lib*) Having two or more separate racks is helpful——makes it more difficult for the boss goats to boss.

Feeding restricted amounts of protein/energy supplements in not easily done even when adequate trough space is available (12 linear inches/adult). Gracious, equitable sharing is simply not a caprine characteristic; greed, aggression, and sheer size conspire against the more civil and/or smaller goats. What to do? You cannot build enough troughs or scatter them far enough; forget that.

Pouring pellets or corn on the ground (at a rapid pace) offers some hope for equity but also encourages waste and parasitism and may occasionally endanger the pourer. I have also tried such feeds in long, hanging vee troughs with goat initially locked out. I open the gate, avoid the rush, and then wait until the timid ones congregate near or outside the gate. Then I offer them pellets in other, nearby vee troughs on the ground. A few still will simply not get their share, but, if they survive and do reasonably well, I brag on them as easy-keepers even as I look for buyers.

I have also tried self-fed supplements, e.g., 80-85% cottonseed meal or soybean meal, 5% calcium carbonate and salt – use 10% initially and later up it to 15% to limit their voluntary intake to an average of 1.0 pound/head/day. This amount will supply about 1/3 pound protein which is over half the protein needed by a pregnant doe; the remaining protein can be had from grass hay or dry grass. Getting such a mix made in small volumes is sometimes a problem; I do it on the feed-room floor with a shovel – even in winter this procedure requires about one Bud-lite/cwt.

Of course, feeding of "complete" or "all-in-one" mixtures neatly solves the problem of equitable intake for all except the most stupid goats. One can offer *ad lib* a custom blend of ground/chopped hay, corn, protein meal, and minerals (and possibly molasses for palatability and for dust control). Your goats will do wonderfully well while your spouse will find it ever so convenient to feed; you, however, will find it considerably less convenient to obtain and to pay for. Definitely not a good option; live with it.

Economics of Feeding Supplements

The cost-benefit ratios to be realized from winter feeding of protein/energy supplements are influenced by duration of feeding and by daily feed costs (supplement plus hay/browse/dry grass) as well as income (the number, size, and price/pound of animals sold during the year). This topic is simply too large to discuss fully in this limited space. However, for "ball-barking purposes", practical experience and realistic estimates seem to show that the *total annual operating costs* of maintaining a breeding doe should be *held under* 50% of the income to be received from the sale of two slaughter kids weighing about 50 pounds each. If this figure cannot be realized, the goat enterprise will likely to be unprofitable. For example, if the income from the net sale of the two kids were $110 and if the annual doe cost were held to, say, $53 (48%), the difference between the income/outgo, $57, is the total return to capital investment, labor, and management/profit. Realistically, if you could keep $35 or so of the $57 for your efforts/profit, you would be considered a successful goat entrepreneur.

And now to the central question, how much of this estimated $53 doe expense/year could you spend on feed for wintering a doe? Let us count the ways...*conservatively*, 3 pounds/day of grass hay for 120 days at, say, 4 cents/pound is $14.40. A pound of 20% protein supplement/head/day is 120 pounds times 12 cents/pound is also $14.40.... plus a bit more for minerals, say, a total of $30/head....which, subtracted from $53, leaves a mere $23 to cover *all other operating costs*....tight, tight...think here of vet bills, utilities, repairs, maintenance, taxes, vehicle charges, etc...aarrgghh, as Lucy and Peanuts were wont to say. But, in any case, be of good cheer...you *could* share a part or all of "your $35 earnings" to cover an operating deficit. Indeed, just knowing that many goat owners routinely do so share may provide you a bit of needed solace during critical periods of economic remorse. However, it will not so comfort your banker which, of course, is a major impetus for you having a decent day job, as also your spouse if you have children as well as kids.

CHAPTER THIRTY-EIGHT

Observations on the Art and Economics of Selling Meat Goats

I n a companion piece in this section entitled, So You Want To Do Meat Goats, I made the point that the prospects for, and the logistics of, marketing one's slaughter goats should receive early and on-going consideration because astute marketing is, economically speaking, as important to the success of a goat enterprise as are procurement of foundation stock and management strategies. Unfortunately, there is much more, and more reliable, public information available on breeding, feeding, and medicating one's goats than information concerning strategies for marketing them. Having realized this deficiency early on, my colleagues and I subsequently undertook a series of projects to investigate various aspects of goat marketing; certain of the results are used below.

This paper updates information concerning goat marketing practices, statistics, industry developments through early 2004. Some of its findings have been previously reported by me, and others, in various publications and at gatherings of goat producers. I am indebted to a number of investigators, early and late, regarding goat production, marketing, carcass work, grading standards, and industry statistics. I gratefully acknowledge the assistance of those in the industry who have shared their experiences and observations with me (some more freely, and a few less accurately, than others). Investigating marketing of goats and goat meat is difficult at best, and at its worse, can be construed as a business intrusion or invasion of personal privacy. Accordingly, I am thankful that those few who declined to share information with me did so with a minimum of mal-ice— I am much too old and way too fat for rapid retreats.

Any analysis of the marketing of a commodity, from gin to goat meat, describes three major components: supply, demand, and channels. For convenience, I begin with the supply sector.

Meat Goat Supply

The supply of goats used for meat consumption in the U.S. includes meat-types (Spanish, Boer crosses, and others), fiber types (Angora and Cashmere) and dairy types (Nubian, Alpine, etc); it also includes import-ed goat carcasses of whatever type and country of origin. Currently, only TX reports an annual census of goats; other States or Universities provide occasional estimates. Latest TX data reflect a decrease in Angora goat numbers from 1,490,000 in 1994 to 220,000 in 2004 (due primarily to the federally mandated demise of the mohair subsidy program in 1995) and compensatory increases in Spanish goat numbers, from 470,000 in 1994 to 980,000 in 2004 (but note in particular the recent drop from the peak of 1,200,000 reached in 2000, as shown in Figure 1). Recovery, and further gains, in TX meat goat numbers now seem questionable, but the southeastern States, already rapidly increasing their goat numbers, could possibly do even more to enlarge national supply.

Currently, the national goat population is thought to be about 2,400,000 head (nearly 1,000,000 TX meat goats and about 250,000 Angora goats in TX and elsewhere) and possibly 750,000 meat goats in other States plus perhaps 400,000 dairy goats. The annual off-take of slaughter goats from this inventory is impossible to compute because only the kill in Federally-inspected plants is reported (647,000 in 2003). In addition to the kill in other, non-reporting venues, there is a very large informal ("backyard") kill; altogether, possibly over 200,000 annually. We also import, mostly from Australia, frozen goat carcasses (well over 500,000 in 2003, up from 124,000 in 1994). Thus we may have con-sumed at least 1,350,000 goats in 2003.

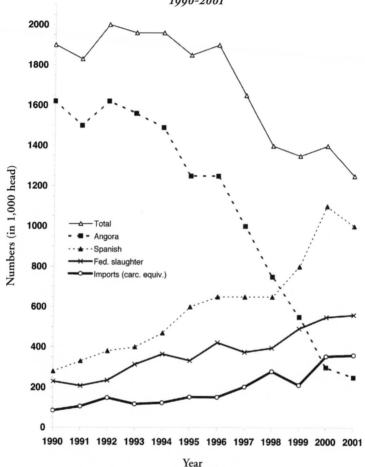

FIGURE I

Goat Inventory, Slaughter and Imports

1990-2001

Goat Meat Demand

No statistics are available to document national demand for goat meat. However, demand may be inferred from known slaughter numbers, import quantities, and estimates of informal kill. Conversations with players in the northeastern metropolitan trade indicate occasional shortages of domestic and imported goat meat. Moreover, present demand seems to be outstripping supply as indicated by record high prices for goats and increased imports. In any case, foreseeable demand is thought to be trending steadily upward, probably in loose concert with the rapidly increasing ethnic population numbers and improved earnings per family. In point of fact, the demand for goat meat is largely ethnic driven. (I define an ethnic as any person, or group, whose ancestors got here after mine did; Native Americans must find the whole who-is-an-ethnic conundrum confusing, perhaps even amusing).

Adherents to the Muslim religion, regardless of geopolitical origin, and the burgeoning urban Latino populations are our primary consumers of goat meat. However, Orientals, Afro-Americans, Haitians and other Caribbean Islanders, as well as those of eastern European origin are also appreciable consumers. Our major goat meat markets are concentrated in the urbanized areas along the northeastern seaboard, on the west coast (the Los Angeles basin, San Francisco, and Seattle), and in inland cities (Atlanta, Dallas, Houston, San Antonio, Chicago, Detroit, Cleveland, and Minneapolis). All these areas contain large concentrations of ethnic groups, and several are currently major immigration target sites. Accordingly, future goat markets seem assured, unless, of course, the ethnic young should opt out irretrievably for burgers, pizza, and KFC—as, indeed, some are already doing.

There are certain discernible patterns in goat meat demand. There is a substantial base demand for goat meat across the entire year, but there *are* seasonal differences, demand being higher in the winter than in summer with fall and spring being intermediate. Cultural holidays, religious or political in origin, create short-duration peaks in demand, usually with concomitant price spikes for consumers and, to a lesser extent, producers.

There are also patterns in consumer demand for certain carcass characteristics. Some groups prefer rather specific weights; for example, Muslims generally prefer carcasses 25-35 lb, while Latinos prefer smaller carcasses, particularly cabrito (little goat) weighing 10-18 lb from milk-fed kids; they do, however, take many larger, thinner (cheaper) animals. Preferred carcass weights for the Christmas and Easter markets range 14-22 lbs. Bucks in the 100-200 lb range find a ready market among Jamaicans and Haitians.

Note that ethnic consumers tend to equate small carcass weights with younger age and younger age with more tender meat. Lighter lean meat color in goat carcasses is thought to be closely related to youthfulness and thus to tenderness. Sex of goat seems of lesser consumer concern, partic-

ularly for animals under one year of age. Please be aware that, while trying to develop a Certified Goat Meat Program in 1997 (patterned on
Certified Angus Beef merchandizing), we found that ethnic consumer
sensory taste panels could *not* distinguish between breed-types of kids,
between wethers or doe kids, between light (under 50 lb) and heavy (over
50 lb) kids, or among kids grading prime, choice, or good conformation
(now called USDA/AMS Selections 1, 2, 3). There being no statistically
valid differences, we were unable to proceed.

All we really know concerning any consumer preferences for, or
among, quality (conformation) grades of goat carcasses is that packer buyers in San Angelo and elsewhere demonstrate differing, recurring price
responses to the three live grades; see Figure 2. This data for slaughter
kids/yearlings, 40-80 lb range, reflects price relationships among grades
and between seasons, even as the general price levels rise across years. We
may logically infer that consumers are also paying these premiums (as a
pass-through or, more likely, as a larger, add-on cost by packers).

FIGURE 2

Price for 40-80 ib. kids goats, San Angelo, TX

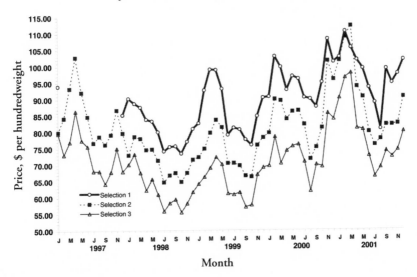

Readers should recognize that the phrase "carcass quality" may have various meanings among goat consumers. Official grading standards for goat carcasses use instead the word "conformation" while many producers prefer the word "condition." All are used to describe the extent of muscling (thickness, plumpness) in a carcass. *Official* USDA graders are also concerned with carcass *proportionality*, i.e., the proper *ratio* of width-to-length with lesser attention to depth (*longer* carcasses must be correspondingly *wider/thicker to achieve an equal grade*). Most consumers, however, seem only to want a "meaty" carcass, i.e., one having an apparently high (visible) meat-to-bone ratio and only minimum external and internal fat.

Certainly, consumers have not, to date, specifically signaled retailers or processors or producers regarding their views on which specific characteristics (larger loin eyes, plumper legs, more marbling, degree of fat covering, boneless yield, etc.) constitute a more desirable goat carcass. Neither have they identified any widespread, pressing needs for primal or retail cuts or for value-added products such as sausages, jerky, ready-to-cook or heat-and-eat items (however, a few such items are currently available at some locations; perhaps availability itself is limiting greater interest).

Readers should also recognize that, currently, consumers seem to have little awareness of, much less preferences for, goat meat from the different breeds or combinations thereof. Carcass quality, however described, seems to be the decisive consideration, along with carcass weight and color, as previously noted. On the other hand, there are now significant numbers of Boer-influence slaughter goats moving through TX and other public auctions. Many industry observers are of the opinion that such crossbreds may now total about 75% of sales; they are also said to constitute a noticeably higher component of the Selections 1 and 2 offerings than do the traditional Spanish goats. But, some of this grade improvement noted might be due to variable environmental influences rather than to breed only; confirming research is badly needed, as are more comparative carcass investigations to validate, under experimental and commercial conditions, claims for superior carcass quality/higher yields and better price responses for newer breed crosses.

Marketing Channels For Goats And Goat Meat

The phrase "goat marketing channels" describes the movement of slaughter goats from the original producer to the final consumer. The major pathways presently used to accomplish this movement are shown in figure 3. Commercial goat channels are relatively simple as compared to those for other species, particularly so from the packer to the final consumer, because probably 90% of goat meat is sold to consumers in the form of hanging carcasses or bone-in cubes. In general, marketing channels with numerous players and those requiring diverse functions will entail more costs than simpler ones. But, goat marketing channels do add costs (collection, handling fees, transportation, weight shrinkage, death loss, slaughter, processing, distribution, retailing, and financing) which, as always, the consumer pays.

FIGURE 3

Producer Meat Goat Marketing Channels

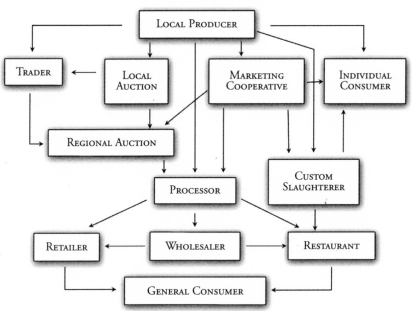

In any case, goat marketing channels do not engender equal treatment and equitably shared profits as between producers and players, nor do they always guarantee final consumers lowest possible prices. As a matter of fact, channel players freely enterprise one another with marked enthusiasm and considerable resourcefulness, treating other players with suspicion and not a little anticipation. Novices to the trade are particularly well-advised to proceed ever so cautiously. A steep, painful learning curve awaits the uninitiated because the free-enterprise system, whose presumed beneficence is so much celebrated in economic theory and political oratory/literature, has no mandated provision for fairness, only for profit-taking. Caveat emptor is a Latin phrase—a warning, and not one to be ignored by greenhorns.

Marketing channel operating costs vary by functions and by players performing them; so also do the profit margins realized by each. Producers delivering goats to an auction pay the cost of transportation, stand the shrink (2 to 3 % of normal farm weight), and pay either a sales commission/head ($3 to $5) or a portion of sales price (3 to 6%) depending on venue. Depending on size of his sale lot, an owner can experience marketing costs of $5 to $7/head, or more. If an owner sells a goat at auction for $1.00/lb, his net price may be only about $.90/lb, farm weight basis. Order buyers/brokers/packing plant employee buyers at auction may add $1.00/head, or more, depending somewhat on purchase volume and post-sale yardage charges.

Subsequent transportation charges/head to distant slaughter facilities vary by load size and mileage rates. Truckers now charge over $2.00/loaded mile for "pot-loads" of about 500 head, TX to NJ, resulting in a transportation cost of at least $7/ head. During this 36-40 hr haul, auction-purchased goats may shrink an addition 4 to 5 % of pay weight (sometimes more, if conditions are extreme). In many cases, pre-slaughter weight at the packer may be only 90% or so of on-farm weight.

Slaughter costs per head vary markedly with kill volume and location; in the NYC area estimates range $8 to $10 but, in smaller southeastern plants, $2-3 higher. The packers add a mark-up of perhaps $7 to $9/head and the retailers typically add 30% of their carcass cost to set consumer prices needed to cover costs and profit. Remember, both operating and profit margins in any food business increase the closer the firms are to the consumer; goat meat is no exception. Thus, it is quite common for a NYC consumer to pay nearly $4.00/lb for goat meat (whole carcass basis) from a goat that sold in TX for only $1.20/lb (be reminded that a 65 lb farm goat typically yields only about 28 lb of retail bone-in meat (43% salable yield, farm-weight basis).

Readers should note that aggregate marketing costs are almost independent of prices paid to producers; a cheaper goat doesn't cost less to haul or kill or merchandize. A 10% cut in producer price from $1.00 to $.90/lb on a 70 lb goat ($7/head) would lower the packer's cost of the cold, shrunk 30 lb carcass by about $.23/lb. The packer might voluntarily share this saving with his retailers, and they might share with their customers (consumers)—but this would likely be so only if effective competition forced all players to follow along. Producer skepticism about this is well known, and deservedly so; as earlier noted, entrepreneurial charity is only a sometime thing.

Producer Options For Increasing Goat Prices/Pound

Goat producers, like other livestock entrepreneurs, are rarely satisfied with prices received for their offerings. Presently, they are caught between an upper price limit (the retail price of goat meat at which very price-sensitive ethnic consumers would shift to alternative meats) and a lower price limit which is probably being adversely influenced by the increasing quantities of cheaper imported goat meat available to those urban areas with high per capita consumption.

Typically, goat producers may increase profits only by reducing their costs of production or, if resources warrant, by increasing enterprise size and output. However, even superior managers finally encounter irreducible limits to such cost reductions. Accordingly, increased farm gate prices must be considered as a possible alternative for increasing net income. Barring U.S. Government interventionist legislation to (try to) reduce goat meat import tonnage via quotas and tariffs, there seem to be but five beneficial marketing options to improve income per lb sold.

First, individual producers could try to cajole higher prices per lb by offering traditional buyers "more desirable goats", e.g., specified body weights, superior conformation grades, greater group uniformity, and programmed delivery dates. Given an individual producer's volume of such offerings and the traditional resistance to on-farm buying (and selling), this option would likely be difficult in practice, if not in theory.

Second, a producer could join with other producers, informally, or in more formal federations or cooperatives, to offer larger volumes of sorted or graded goats, in a timely manner, to multiple, competing individual buyers for negotiated, fairer prices. The premise of such cooperative endeavors, however structured, is to create countervailing market power, i.e., organize volume sellers to bargain with entrenched, volume buyers. Historically, Agricultural Cooperatives have been both philosophically appealing and theoretically efficient; contrarily, implementation has frequently been pure hell, and the duration of many painfully short. The basic reason for this is that sustained cooperation within a group requires more personal tolerance, patience, and good will than many individuals can give – or take.

Third, producers (individually or cooperatively) could possibly mimic a recently adopted cattle marketing strategy and retain ownership of their goats beyond the ranch as they move to slaughter and possibly to, or even through, retailing activities. Note that, unlike typical cattle movements, relatively few goats now go to commercial slaughter via a post-farm stocker (grow-out) period and/or a feed-lot finishing period. Nevertheless, a retained ownership strategy, possibly in conjunction with stocker/finisher operations (for adding size and /or condition or for holding to better match supply/demand situations) might accord well with a producer-owned packer and possibly even a producer-owned distribution system to retail stores. Impartial investigations to validate this premise would be a valuable contribution to goat industry development, but one not likely to occur.

Fourth, producers might elect to modify their current management practices, particularly breeding/kidding times, to supply goats of preferred weights and grades during the historically higher priced winter markets. As always, agro climatic conditions and any other limiting factors, including cost-benefit ratios, would be crucial concerns for implementing novel production or marketing strategies.

Fifth, individual goat producers might, in certain situations, sell directly to the final consumer rather than into the traditional marketing system. Such direct marketing is the most efficient, least costly option available because it eliminates any further selling costs…no hauling, no shrink, no commission. Perhaps equally important, it provides opportunity for the producer to negotiate the price of his goats appreciably beyond the prevailing auction prices. Moreover, the opportunity for the customer to kill his goat according to his cultural dictates at his preferred time and circumstance is a valuable consideration.

Readers should recognize, however, that direct marketing does have some possible constraints, e.g., the distance between seller and buyer may be limiting. Also, prospective buyers may not be aware of the availability of saleable goats on area farms. Too, there may be, in some jurisdictions, legal prohibitions against slaughter on the seller's farm or, alternatively, even on the buyer's property. Because only anecdotal evidence exists concerning the practicality of direct marketing in sufficient volume to be economical, individual producers ought to carefully evaluate such an opportunity for site-specific benefits and constraints.

For those unwilling, or unable, to do direct marketing, it might be possible for them to sell a goat for a negotiated price including delivery to a local custom slaughter facility where the new owner would take custody, arrange the slaughter, and pay associated costs. A version of direct selling is sometimes done by a producer who sells goats to a distant entrepreneur who then sells them to customers coming to his site (usually conveniently close to urban areas having numerous interested ethnics—the TX/CA shuffle comes to mind).

Summary

1) The supply of goats from all sources, domestic and imported, continues to increase but may now be lagging behind aggregate demand.

2) The vast majority of demand for goat meat comes from ethnic populations, however defined.

3) Most goat meat sold at retail is not offered in primal or retail cuts, but rather is merchandized as bone-in cubes or whole, half, or quarter carcasses.

4) There is substantial informal slaughter, perhaps as much as 30 % of production, either on-farm or at buyer's premises.

5) The meat goat industry is characterized by many small and a few large, but scattered, producers remote from the few packers who, in turn, tend to be relatively close to retail outlets most often located in highly urbanized areas.

6) Modest price differentials are now being paid by packers to producers for goats graded USDA Selections 1, 2, and 3; however, these differentials (about 10 cents/pound), tend to expand or contract somewhat depending on demand levels across time and place.

7) Producer prices have been trending upward for the past several years and are currently at all-time highs for all classes of slaughter goats.

Conclusions

1) For as long as it remains economically feasible (sufficiently profitable) to do so, producers should continue to provide an ever increasing supply of goats to the ethnic, and other, markets. Goats should have sufficient quality to exceed that of our competition from imports, and also to meet any developing demand for better and more consistent quality from our institutional trade.

2) In order for producers to economically grow heavier, consistently high quality goats (USDA Selections 1 and 2) to be targeted toward the nascent, slowly evolving supermarket and "white table cloth" trade, they would necessarily have to receive premium prices (get a more equitable share of the consumer dollar). The present volumes, precise needs, and future potential for this novel trade are not known, our national foodservice sector has been willing to pay premium prices for consistent and standardized meat cuts from other livestock species.

3) Some goat producers feel that packers/processors could—and should—develop and merchandize value-added products in addition to their bulk carcass trade. Because the usable boneless yield of cheaper, larger goats is only 25-30% of live weight and because further processing procedures add labor and manufacturing costs, these end-products would likely have to be sold at substantial premiums/pound over alternative forms of goat meat. Ethnics might or might not accept these products initially or pay the necessary premiums. Goat meat jerky, sausages, oven-ready fabricated roasts, and heat-and-eat products are, to date, mostly prospects only—to ethnic and non-ethnic alike. But, even if such premiums for value-added products were to be realized by processors/retailers, there is no effective mechanism to force them to share equitably with goat producers. Be careful here because, in the beef and pork trade, higher grading, more expensive animals are not normally used for value-added products. Is there any reason to think it would be any different with goats?

4) Because of the real nutritional benefits of goat meat (high quality protein, low total fat and lower saturated fat) and also its (incorrectly) assumed benefit of low cholesterol, some feel that this is an exploitable avenue into Health Food markets with their typically high prices (which, currently, producers could only hope to share). Again, care is urged, there being too little evidence that typical goat meat consumers also are frequent Health Food customers.

5) Producers could possibly guarantee themselves a more equitable share of the consumer goat meat dollar via cooperative ownership of collection points, transport units, packing facilities, and distribution routes to retailers—almost a pasture-to-plate scheme, but with very demanding group and personal characteristics and one that is also very capital intensive.

Addendum

Another way for goat producers to possibly help themselves might be provision of funds to appropriate research entities with a view to developing (among other things) value-added product technology. Returns to producers could be directly realized via licensing fees and (less likely) indirectly realized via improvements in sale numbers and/or in prices/lb received. Such producer self-help funds could be generated by voluntary donations to/through local, state, or national associations or, perhaps more realistically, by assessments on head or weight basis at cooperating "first-sale" points. Instituting a mandatory check-off system via the USDA is an alternative getting current, but preliminary, attention. Other livestock groups are using versions of this system, but effective results and producer satisfaction have not been uniformly achieved, some being judged better than others. In any case, initiating such a program is politically difficult (given the recent history of other livestock check-off programs), time-consuming, and costly. If it were passed and implemented, the (suggested) deduction of $.50/goat probably would not be a burden, particularly to owners of the typically small flocks in eastern TX and in the Southeast. As always, efficient and effective use of the collected funds (demonstrable, favorable results) would be the crucial consideration for sustained operation.

Lastly, goat producers could individually or, much better, collectively petition (jaw-bone?) politicians and University agricultural research personnel to allocate State-approved research funds to goat product development and corollary marketing studies; in effect, to directly compete with the other livestock sectors for attention and budget. For your information, most federal and many state agricultural research dollars are now allocated, via USDA fiat, to basic science/fundamental investigations and (to solving) high-visibility problems having state or national significance and, therefore, political attention. Relatively few funds are currently spent on applied, practical animal research projects. Goats, being a minority species with fewer and less vocal supporters (voters), are critically under-represented at decision-making levels. Consequently, goat research and, especially, corollary extension efforts are short-changed; no squeaky wheel, no grease, etc.

CHAPTER THIRTY-NINE

Profiling the U.S. Goat Industry

Preface

T he primary purpose of this article is to acquaint readers concerning certain structural and operational aspects of the current goat industry. Many industry players, potential players, and agriculturally oriented observers in general are seemingly only partially informed about the major categories and primary purposes of the various types of goat enterprises. Accordingly, those considering getting into goats or expanding their present enterprise (in scale and/or scope) could possibly benefit from a brief, informal review of historical and current goat enterprise characteristics.

Historical Context

Original European settlers coming to eastern coastal America brought "dual-purpose" goats (for milk and meat), while settlers from Spain to Mexico and, later, to Texas brought goats primarily for meat and hide production. The descendents of this latter source became known as Spanish or Spanish-type goats (and, as they subsequently migrated to the southern states, they were called brush or briar or hill goats). Angora goats from Turkey were introduced around 1900 and, shortly thereafter, became concentrated in lesser rainfall areas of Texas, primarily the Edwards Plateau northwest of San Antonio. In those geographic areas where the major types of imported goats came to co-mingle socially (purposefully or not), unfettered crossbreeding was the norm; therefore, one should recognize that "purebred goat" was, early on, necessarily a very relative descriptive term. In point of fact, this situation is not greatly different today, despite the recent introduction and rapid spread of exotic purebred breeds from various venues.

Dairy Goats

During the past century, goats held primarily for production of fluid milk and cheese production became widely diffused across much of the U. S. There are six recognized breeds (Alpine, Saanen, Toggenburg, Nubian, LaMancha, and Oberhasli). Aggregate numbers of "dairy-type" goats are not precisely known, but current industry observers commonly suggest about 400 thousand head nationwide with the Nubian and Alpine purebreds/grades being the most prevalent. The three Swiss breeds (Alpine, Saanen, and Toggenburg) typically provide higher yields of milk but with lower % fat and % protein components as compared to the Nubian breed, while the LaMancha and Oberhasli breeds are intermediate to these groups in yield and composition. In any case, surplus kids and unproductive animals from all these breeds enter the national goat meat marketing channels, either directly from the farm or via auction venues.

Nubians and Nubian crosses are usually thought to provide the "meatiest" carcasses; however, bloomy young milk-fed kids of any dairy breed typically command a better price than meat-type goats of similar age/size (at least prior to the Boer goat phenomenon). Note that a considerable portion of the male dairy kids may not be retained and raised for meat purposes because of unfavorable economic ratios, i.e., the milk required to raise a kid to weaning at 8-12 weeks of age may have more value as fluid milk/cheese than as feed for kids). But, given the recent high prices for young, high quality slaughter kids, this situation may be changing. Experienced slaughter-goat market watchers know that older cull dairy goats typically have brought less money per pound than meat-type goats of similar age and size; nowadays, however, dairy goats in *good* condition (but definitely not fat) usually garner near comparable prices.

And, finally, readers should recognize that over the years many Texas (and other) owners of "pure" Spanish goats purposefully used dairy sires (particularly Nubian and, to a lesser extent, Alpine and Toggenburg) to increase kid size and milk yield of the crosses. Indeed, original/pure Spanish goats are increasingly rare in many areas due to these introduced admixtures of dairy goat and, more recently, Boer goat genes. The introduction of dairy goat genes to the typical Spanish-type herd sometimes resulted in unintended consequences, e.g., overly large and pendulous udders, increased doe size/reduced stocking rates, and reduced hardiness/decreased % kid crop (born or weaned), particularly under poor range conditions.

Angora Goats

Although not as prevalent as wool and lamb production, production of mohair from Angora goats under extensive range conditions was a mainstay of Texas ranching for most of the 20th century. Peak Angora goat numbers (5.5 million) were reached in the mid-sixties, but thereafter gradually fell, for various reasons, to just under 2 million by the mid-nineties. With the demise in 1995 of the USDA Wool and Mohair Act, numbers precipitously declined, but have seemingly stabilized at 225,000 head or so in the recent past. Small numbers of Angora goats are still found in NM and AZ, but the modest surge in mohair production seen in OK, MI and MO seen during the eighties has all but disappeared.

From 1955 to 1995, Angora goat enterprises generated mohair for sale at world market prices and for mostly international usage. However, mohair producers received additional, substantial income via the Wool and Mohair Act—essentially a subsidy program funded with tariff monies collected on wool imported from Australia and New Zealand. Actual "support prices" varied widely across time, ranging from zero to over 100% of world-price levels, depending on various USDA-calculated formula components. As may be imagined, domestic and international politics were an integral part of this program throughout its long life.

As always, kid 'hair commands the highest prices (currently $5-6/lb) while yearling 'hair commands much lesser prices (under $3/lb); adult 'hair provides by far the largest volumes of enterprise sales but commands the lowest prices (just under $2/lb). Fiber diameter and other quality factors are the primary determinants of selling prices at various demand levels. Adult mohair yields currently range between 8 and 10 pounds per animal per year and kids clip from 1 to 2 pounds annually with yearling yields intermediate at 3-5 pounds/head/year.

Angora goat enterprises also generate income from the sale of surplus breeding stock and from the salvage value of animals culled for poor mohair yield and/or quality or because of forced herd reduction due to intermittently poor range conditions. Such "culls" move via various marketing channels to slaughter and on to consumers. Until the mid-eighties, the vast majority of domestic goat meat eaten by urban consumers was from Angora goats with Spanish-type goats and dairy stock supplying the remainder. Currently, the major supply of goat meat comes from "meat-type" goats with perhaps the largest component of the annual national kill being Boer-cross animals.

Presently, the typical yields of mohair and relatively low prices for adult mohair, together with relatively low slaughter prices/lb, conspire to generate rather low gross income (per head) to an Angora goat enterprise. Accordingly, minimizing costs of production inputs is absolutely essential to achieve even modest returns to labor, management, and capital.

Meat Goats

As indicated previously, for many years Texas goat enterprises focused on production of mohair from Angora stock. But, many such enterprises also raised varying, indeterminate numbers of Spanish-type goats, mostly for on-farm consumption or for direct "meat" sales off-farm. At times, somewhat larger volumes were sold through local auctions; such animals might be bought and transported considerable distances for slaughter, while others might be purchased by area ranchers looking for replacement stock or for brush/weed control. Scattered small herds of Spanish-type goats were also raised and similarly merchandized by farmers in the southeastern states and elsewhere. All such goats were usually minimally managed, if at all, with very limited inputs throughout the year. Consequently, reproductive efficiencies, off-take rates, and average weaning weights were typically quite low; not surprisingly, such practices frequently resulted in little or no profit to owners.

For some 25 years following WWII, 3-5 month old weanling goats weighing from 20/40 pounds could be bought at farms and ranches for perhaps $3-7/head, but by the early eighties such goats were selling for about $12-15/head. Thereafter, as Angora goat numbers continued to decline, Spanish-type goats slowly increased both in quantity and value with slaughter kids worth perhaps $18-20/head—or more, at certain holiday periods. By the early nineties, light weight Texas slaughter kids were bringing around $30/head but, as Angora goat numbers fell precipitously after 1995, slaughter kid prices began to move sharply upward. In response to this novel marketing incentive, numbers of meat-type goats also increased markedly as producers began to use better production practices to improve both the scale and the efficiency of their growing meat goat enterprises.

Starting in the mid-nineties when Boer goat genetics were introduced and became increasingly available, widespread crossbreeding with Spanish-type goats began. By 2003, industry players in Texas estimated that about 75% of slaughter kids moving at public auctions demonstrated Boer goat influence. Currently, considerable uncertainty exists among commercial goat owners as to the proper percentage of Boer in their base doe herd, but, generally, the feeling is that the better the forage base, the higher the percentage Boer permissible. In any case, there are very few "full Boer" commercial meat goat operations to date. The Kiko breed, introduced from New Zealand in the early nineties, has also been used in various venues for crossbreeding/upgrading and for purebred production (as has the genetically programmed myotonic Tennessee Meat Goat). A number of southeastern entrepreneurs have used Boer bucks as terminal sires on Kiko x Spanish crosses to good effect. Readers should recognize that the volume of industry speculation far exceeds any necessary "proof-of-the-pudding" data as regards the economically optimum choice among the many crossbreeding program options available to producers everywhere.

"*Commercial meat goat*" enterprises, which account for the overwhelming majority of national numbers, may be conveniently, if imprecisely, characterized as to purpose, scale, and scope. Their primary purpose is to produce slaughter kids, but they may also generate surplus foundation (breeding) animals for sale; moreover, about 20% of the doe herd is sold annually as cull animals. These enterprises may range in size from less than a 100 to a 1,000 does (or more), but, large or small, nearly all feature "extensive" pasture or range management schemes using native, perennial grasses and/or browse, plus minimum supplemental protein and energy feeds as forage availability decreases seasonally. Generally speaking, health care costs tend to rise with increasing rainfall levels across extensively (and intensively) managed venues. On the other hand, the poorer the average rainfall, the greater the tendency to select smaller, hardier breeds or their crossbreds as the base herd (in order to compensate for limited forage yields and quality).

Well-managed commercial enterprises can, over the years, generate weaned kid crops (average kid weight 40/45 lbs) ranging from 100 to 130 % per year under extensive conditions (from a mixed-age doe herd). To achieve higher weaning rates (150% and up) and also get atypically heavier weaning weights (50-60 lbs), managers would have to increase production inputs substantially; if so, the resultant cost-benefit ratios realized usually justify such strategies, but not always. Commercially managed does usually kid between 12 and 18 months of age and typically average five sets of kids before going to slaughter (or dying) at 6-7 years of age; productive 9-10 year old does are rather rare. Infertility, bad udders, low milk production, poor mothering ability, disease, parasites, predators, etc. all contribute to disappearance rates of does. A majority of extensively managed herds have historically run bucks with the does year round. This typically results in a large kidding wave Thanksgiving/late February with a much smaller wave in mid-April/late May; however, given the recent price incentives for kids born "out-of-season", some changes in kidding seasons may become advantageous.

Regarding the economics of commercial kid production, three crucial management factors largely determine the *break-even price* of a kid at sale time. These are: the annual maintenance cost of the does, the percent kid crop sold, and the weight/condition of the kids. The profit per kid is calculated as the dollar difference between its break-even price and its net sale price (after all sale expenses including transportation). Readers should realize that commercial, extensively-managed goat enterprises vary widely in their average annual doe maintenance cost, but, if this cost can not be held below $50, it will be difficult to realize acceptable profit levels. It would also be difficult if the enterprise could not average at least 150% kid crop sold. See table 1 for a telling demonstration of the effects of these management factors on the break-even price/lb of kid weight sold. For example, *for 50 lb weaning weight kids*.... from a doe whose maintenance

∞

FIGURE 1

Influence of selling weight of kids
on break-even selling price per pound.

DOE COST	KID CROP WEANED						
$/hd/yr	75%	100%	125%	150%	175%	200%	225%
			BREAKEVEN PRICE, $/LB:				
(Selling weight: 50 lb/hd)							
30	.80	.60	.48	.40	.34	.30	.27
35	.93	.70	.56	.47	.40	.35	.31
40	1.07	.80	.64	.53	.46	.40	.36
45	1.20	.90	.72	.60	.51	.45	.40
50	1.33	1.00	.80	.67	.57	.50	.44
55	1.47	1.10	.88	.73	.63	.55	.49
60	1.60	1.20	.96	.80	.69	.60	.53
65	1.73	1.30	1.04	.87	.74	.65	.58
70	1.87	1.40	1.12	.93	.80	.70	.62
(Selling weight: 60 lb/hd)							
30	.67	.50	.40	.33	.29	.25	.22
35	.78	.58	.47	.39	.33	.29	.26
40	.89	.67	.53	.44	.39	.33	.30
45	1.00	.75	.60	.50	.43	.38	.33
50	1.11	.83	.67	.56	.48	.42	.37
55	1.22	.92	.73	.61	.52	.46	.41
60	1.33	1.00	.80	.67	.57	.50	.44
65	1.44	1.08	.87	.72	.62	.54	.48
70	1.56	1.17	.93	.78	.67	.58	.52
(Selling weight: 70 lb/hd)							
30	.57	.43	.34	.29	.24	.21	.19
35	.67	.50	.40	.33	.29	.25	.22
40	.76	.57	.46	.38	.33	.29	.25
45	.86	.64	.51	.43	.37	.32	.29
50	.95	.71	.57	.48	.41	.36	.32
55	1.05	.79	.63	.52	.45	.39	.35
60	1.14	.86	.69	.57	.49	.43	.38
65	1.24	.93	.74	.62	.53	.46	.41
70	1.33	1.00	.80	.67	.57	.50	.44

cost was $50/year and which produced a 150% kid crop, the breakeven price/lb for the 1.5 kids (75 lbs selling weight) would be $.6733. If the 75 lbs sold for a *net* $1.00/lb, the profit/lb would be $.3333 and thus $25.00/doe/yr ($75-50).

Readers should understand that an *accurate* annual maintenance cost/doe can be calculated only if *all* expenses of the goat enterprise are totaled for the year and divided by the number of breeding age does in the herd on January 1. It is recommended, however, that you personally undertake such a challenging and likely enervating calculation only if you have a high pain threshold and no history of cardiac difficulties. Believe it or not, $30/40 profit/doe/year in commercial operations would be considered *very acceptable indeed* by their owners (and a figment of their imagination by goat-country bankers).

In addition to the commercial slaughter goat enterprises just described, there are a number of other types of goat enterprises which together account for a substantial part of the national meat goat population. They may be conveniently categorized by their primary purposes, as explained below.

"Purebred meat goat enterprises" are those which generate purebred, "registered" animals primarily for sale as breeding stock. Currently, purebred Boer goat herds and their aggregate numbers far exceed the counts of purebred Kiko, TMG, Savannahs, etc.; there are, of course, no "purebred' Spanish goats. Knowledgeable industry players/observers are able to distinguish, however imperfectly, among certain sub-categories of purebred goat enterprises. They do this by making comparisons concerning an owners' major Show "placings", who sells to/buys from whom and at what prices, who has the most popular bloodlines, who bought from what country-of-origin, breeder reputation, etc. Descriptive terms such as *Breeders* of *Foundation Stock or Seed Stock Producers, or Elite Breeders* are used to denote this relatively small group of players.

From these elite herds, a second tier of breeders purchase foundation stock in order to expand numbers which are then offered for sale to each other, to other (usually) smaller breeders, and to the much more numerous producers of commercial goats wishing to "upgrade" their herds via use of purebred sires. Looking nationally, one can discern still other subcategories of purebred Boer goat enterprises—largely by noting certain characteristics: size of operation, prices levels paid/received, marketing targets, extent of participation in local, regional, or national Shows, attendance at local and regional Field Days, Seminars, etc.

"*Smallholder meat goat enterprises*" account for a fairly substantial, but growing, portion of the national meat goat herd. Most tend to be *intensively managed* operations with much smaller herd sizes and land resources employed as contrasted to the *extensively managed* commercial operations earlier described. If well-managed, average herd performance, as measured by off-take, sales prices received, cash flow, and net profit, can exceed that of larger extensive operations (on a per head basis).

Herd sizes usually range from 25 to 100 does, and stocking rates of 5/10 head per acre are not uncommon. Such enterprises are widely dispersed, from eastern Texas throughout the southeast and, increasingly, in the northeast, mid-Atlantic, and elsewhere. Smallholder enterprises typically utilize Spanish-type goats or crossbreds as their base herd and use purebred bucks, of whatever breed, to produce kids for the slaughter market (or other sales targets). While such enterprises are *intended* to at least breakeven or yield at least a modest annual profit, some do, some do not (especially when inequitable marketing opportunities are encountered). In any case, there is great variation within and between smallholder herds over time and place as to production and marketing practices, as also to economic viability.

In those cases in which such enterprises remain unprofitable over time, they are more accurately described as *hobby* goat operations. And, while these may be consistently losing appreciable money, hobbyists may also be garnering many "non-cash" satisfactions from goat ownership activities…the phrases: fun time, family interaction, shared responsibility, constructive work, personal dependability, cooperative endeavors, appreciation for nature, enjoyable exercise, learning experiences, etc. are often heard concerning such endeavors. At the end of the day, one can ask, but rarely get a precise answer to the question of: just how valuable, really, *is* this goat experience? Be that as it may, the annual off-take from such herds does contribute substantially to the national kill.

"*Wether goat enterprises*" are a fairly new, but increasingly important, segment of the meat goat industry. While Texas leads the nation in number of 4-H/FFA youth projects featuring wethers shown in weight-based slaughter classes at organized, premium-paying Shows, project numbers are now expanding sharply in other states as well. Note that the recommended practices for selection, management, fitting, showing, and judging of project animals may be quite variable within and between states, but, in any case, virtually all the animals are finally sold for slaughter.

Indeed, the annual national kill of such goats has been estimated to be around 100,000 head (for comparison, the total *federally*-inspected goat kill in 2003 was 647,000 head).

Readers should understand that the stated purpose/objective of such projects is, generally speaking, youth education (however locally defined). Wether goat projects only rarely realize a profit, i.e., return a sum exceeding the cost of the goat, feed bill, health care, etc. unless, of course, the animal places sufficiently high in the contest to attract unusually high bids from the post-Show public sale. Such buyers, be they businessmen, professionals, or doting grandparents, are prone to pay prices well beyond slaughter values. Such inflated prices, in turn, encourage ever higher prices to be paid for prospective project goats the following year.

Consequently, astute entrepreneurs seek to meet this demand by creating superior show prospects via genetic selection and improved management. Indeed, there are now a number of enterprises whose paramount purpose is to provide Show prospects for this emerging market; however, a much greater numbers of purebred enterprises and smallholder operations also engage in this endeavor, as a corollary to their major activities.

Readers should be aware that there is considerable, on-going industry discussion/dispute regarding the most desirable phenotype ("the looks") of wethers for Shows. Requiring follow-up carcass evaluations to visually compare and mathematically correlate *live placings* with *carcass placings* would seem to be a most useful procedure to *objectively* identify those Show and/or carcasses characteristics of *actual economic concern* to processors and/or consumers.

Conclusion

This article describes the major categories of the national goat industry and briefly characterizes them as to scale, scope, and primary purpose. As seen from the perspective of the last decade, a number of substantial and on-going changes in the goat industry have occurred; as a result, certain future trends now seem discernible. For example:

1) Total goat slaughter in the U.S. seems to be increasing, but not fast enough, as new producers in the southeast and elsewhere increase their off-take in the face of declining Texas goat populations.

2) Total meat-type goat numbers are increasing relative to dairy goats and Angora goats.

3) There has been a noticeable shift from predominantly Spanish-type slaughter goats to crossbred animals showing substantial Boer goat influence.

4) Annual Federal slaughter goat numbers have steadily increased over the last decade; however, a portion of this increase may be only "statistical" (because of on-going reductions in the proportions of goats killed in non-federal venues).

5) Imported goat meat tonnage has steadily increased as domestic production/slaughter has declined relative to ever increasing demand.

6) Ethnic populations (our major consumers of goat meat) are increasing rapidly in total numbers and as a percent of the U.S. population; their disposable income/family is also increasing as they participate more equitably in the work force.

7) Imported goat meat now constitutes roughly one-third of aggregate consumption; this percentage will undoubtedly rise if, as expected, domestic production fails to keep pace with rising demand.

8) More and more goats are being marketed by weight and grade rather than by the head; improvements in prices paid to producers have usually, but not always, reflected this change.

9) The trend in prices received by producers has moved noticeably upward as domestic production has fallen relative to total consumption; the 2003/04 prices for graded slaughter goats of all weights are at an all-time high.

10) Record consumer demand this year has lead to an unusual marketing situation in which producers appear to be selling a substantial portion of their young prospective replacement-quality does for slaughter rather than retaining them for breeding stock in the usual fashion. Should this practice continue over time, it could lead to an even tighter supply of slaughter kids in the coming years and, consequently, to a further increase in consumer prices.(Historically, consumers of other red meats have demonstrated considerable purchasing resistance in certain markets when prices became, in their opinion, exorbitant; such might be the case even among our traditional customers for goat meat).

Dr. McMillin measures the color of muscle tissue,
another carcass characteristic while Dr. Pinkerton looks on.

Dr. Pinkerton labels cuts of meat,
a part of developing USDA grading standards.

CHAPTER FORTY

Industry Update 2006

Continued Goat Population Growth and Other Trends
By Ken McMillin and Frank Pinkerton

Preface

There have been several recent articles elsewhere on the state of the goat industry and prognostications regarding the future demand for goats and goat meat. This 2006 Industry Update is the latest in our series of such reports dating from 1999.

Complete official data from USDA agencies are not available until March each year, but the inventory of Angora, milk, and meat goats is now available from National Agricultural Statistics Service (NASS) every January. The import/export date for bulk, intermediate, and consumer oriented (BICO) foods and beverages, including goat meat, are available in February from the USDA Foreign Agricultural Service. The data for different species slaughtered under federal inspection are published in March.

Introduction

The breeding goat inventories in the U.S. were 1,853,000 meat and 241,500 Angora on January 1, 2006, up 5% and down 1%, respectively, from the January 1, 2005 breeding inventories of 1,762,700 meat and

243,600 Angora (Table 1). The total numbers of all goats (breeding, market, and kid crop) were 2,826,000, up 4% from the previous year total number of 2,715,000.

TABLE I

Goat numbers by class in the United States
January 1, 2005 and 2006.

Goat Class	2006 Head	2005 Head	% change 2005 to 2006
All goats	2,826,000	2,715,000	4.09
Angora goats, total	278,000	280,000	-0.71
Milk goats, total	288,000	285,000	1.05
Meat goats, total	2,260,000	2,150,000	5.12
Meat goats, breeding	1,853,000	1,762,700	5.12
Meat goats, market	407,000	387,300	5.09
Kid crop, total	1,835,700	1,761,000	4.24
Kid crop, meat goats	1,488,100	Not available	Not available

The number of meat and Angora goats marketed in 2005 was 443,500 head compared with 423,700 head marketed in 2004, up 4.7%. These numbers reflect formal reporting of goat sales through only established channels such as auctions or to dealers. They do **not** include the unknown/unknowable thousands of goats sold through informal, non-reporting on-farm and "roadside" sales.

The kid crop born in 2005 increased to 1,835,700 from 1,761,000 born in 2004 (4.2% increase). A very rough "national kid crop percentage" of 81.1% may be calculated by dividing the number of kids born in 2005 by the January 1, 2005 combined (meat and Angora) breeding goat inventory of 2,262,800.

The NASS report on Angora numbers indicates a 1% drop from 2005 to 2006; however, TX, AZ and NM (with 88% of the total) reported little or no change. Note that Angora numbers were 436,000 as recently as 2000 and were 1.386 million head in 1995 (in the mid-sixties, TX alone had about 5.5 million Angora goats).

Meat goat supply

The number of head of meat (and *other*) goats (excluding Angora and dairy) as reported for the top 20 states are shown in table 2. In 2006, Texas had 48% of meat/other goats, while TX and the other top nine states in meat goat numbers had, collectively, 76%; the top 20 states had 89.4%. The table also shows that there was a 5% increase in total meat goat numbers from 2005 with many in the top 20 states showing considerably larger percentage increases. NC and OK had only modest increases this year, but both had substantial increases earlier on; only MS and OH showed a decrease in numbers from 2005. Note that the 5% increase

TABLE 2

Meat and Other Goats, Number by State
January 1, 2005 and 2006.

State	2006 Head	2005 Head	% change 2005 to 2006
Texas	1,030,000	1,080,000	4.85
Tennessee	98,000	103,000	5.10
Georgia	88,500	95,000	7.34
California	75,000	80,000	6.67
Oklahoma	73,000	74,000	1.37
Kentucky	63,500	68,000	7.09
Missouri	60,000	64,000	6.67
North Carolina	59,000	60,000	1.69
Florida	51,500	55,000	6.80
South Carolina	41,000	44,000	7.32
Alabama	40,000	43,000	7.50
Virginia	38,000	41,000	7.89
Pennsylvania	35,200	37,000	5.11
Arkansas	27,000	29,000	7.41
Ohio	29,000	28,000	-3.45
Indiana	23,800	25,000	5.04
Colorado	22,000	24,000	9.09
Mississippi	24,500	24,000	-2.04
Kansas	22,000	23,000	4.55
Washington	21,000	23,000	9.52
All other states	228,000	240,000	5.26
U.S. total	2,150,000	2,260,000	5.12

in meat goat numbers during the past year compares to 2% increases in cattle/calves and sheep/lambs, while hog/pig numbers remained constant.

A word of caution here….all of these USDA numbers were derived by surveying a large, representative sample of goat producers. Statistically speaking, there is a 1 in 10 chance the figures might be off by more than 2% due to sampling errors. Nevertheless, these new annual estimates are a much needed improvement over the historical five-year Census figures.

A further word of caution….it is important to remember that these '06 inventory figures refer to live goats in late 05. They do not recognize the sizeable loss of goats during the year. For instance, in **2004**, a USDA nationwide survey of representative goat owners found that a total of 415,200 adults/kids were lost (nearly 15%, from a population of about 2.7 million). Disease claimed 43.4%, predators took 37.3%, and other causes were 19.3%. Losses of kid goats alone were 286,000 (69%) of the total, and of the kid losses, 40% were taken by predators and 42% by disease.

Figure 1 conveniently demonstrates certain industry supply/demand geographical relations. The nation's premier goat meat market continues to be the contiguous metropolitan areas along Interstate 95 from Washington/Baltimore to Philadelphia to New York City, Providence, and Boston. Other regional urban areas of high goat meat consumption are Los Angeles, San Francisco, Houston/Dallas/San Antonio, Atlanta, Cleveland, Detroit, and Chicago. Metropolitan Miami is also an area of very strong demand for goat meat, but nearly all of it is imported from Australia. Miami is the second largest port for imported goat meat behind Philadelphia.

While TX continues to supply thousands of goats to NJ, NY, and PA for slaughter, TN, KY, NC, and GA also increasingly contribute to this market, now thought to total well over 300,000 annually. Note that substantial portions of TX, GA, FL, and CA slaughter goats are consumed in-state. Although CA produces many goats, it must also bring in goats from TX, OK, and elsewhere; moreover, thousands of Australian goat carcasses are imported to meet its ever-growing demand. San Francisco and Los Angeles imported the 3rd and 4th largest amounts of goat meat in 2005.

As you see from the map and in Table 2, goat numbers have grown, and are still increasing, in those states that are closest to the I-95 metro markets described above. A sort of "directional shift" in production capability, from TX to the southeastern states and into the corn-belt states and old dairy states (PA, NY) seems discernible.

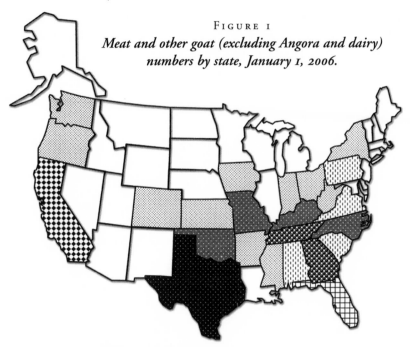

FIGURE 1

Meat and other goat (excluding Angora and dairy)
numbers by state, January 1, 2006.

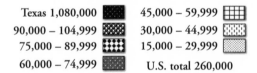

MEAT GOAT NUMBERS BY STATE, 2006

Texas 1,080,000	■	45,000 – 59,999	▦
90,000 – 104,999	▨	30,000 – 44,999	▨
75,000 – 89,999	▨	15,000 – 29,999	▨
60,000 – 74,999	▨	U.S. total 260,000	

Perhaps this shift is being motivated by higher transportation costs from the more remote areas, or by profit-sapping parasite problems in the warm/humid south, or by a pressing need for alternative livestock enterprises above the Mason-Dixon Line. It could also be that more profitable direct-marketing of goats from growing numbers of northeastern small-holder operations to "local" ethnic consumers is increasing sharply **outside** of these huge urban centers.

Goat slaughter

Comparisons of U.S. meat goat numbers, Angora goat numbers, federal slaughter, and imported goat meat are shown in Figure 2. From 1992 until 2002, meat goat numbers increased sharply, from 591,000 to 1,938,000; however, **the annual rate of increase since 2002 seems to be slowing a bit.** Note that the precipitous decline in Angora numbers, dating from the mid-nineties, has also slowed and, since 2002, seems to be stabilizing; **no appreciable recovery is anticipated.**

Numbers of total goats, meat goats and Angora goats in the U.S., total goats in Texas, federal slaughter, and goat meat imports (as 35 pound carcass equivalents).

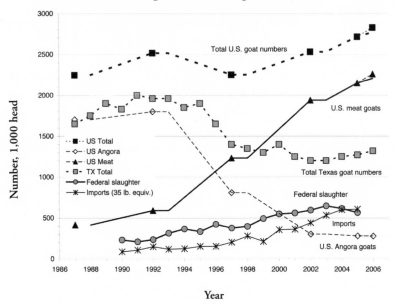

Federal slaughter numbers have declined for the second straight year. The 2005 figure of 566,208 is but 92% of the 2004 figure and only 87% of the 2003 figure. **This mini-trend may/may not continue downward.** Note that some of this reported decline may be "statistical" in nature. Over the past two years, two federally-inspected plants in TX ceased operations, but some portion of their annual kill was subsequently done in state-inspected plants. The smaller of these two plants has only recently resumed federally-inspected slaughter (but with very low volume).

Contrarily, yet another plant recently opened and is now shipping substantial numbers of federally-inspected carcasses. The 2006 federal slaughter figures may well reflect these events.

The quantity of goat meat imported during 2005 (21.3 million pounds, equivalent to 608,020 35-lb carcasses) increased by 225,165 lbs (6,433 carcass equivalents). This 1% increase from 2004 is sharply lower than the average annual increase of 17% from 2000 to 2004. One may **speculate** that Australia's national inventory of feral goats available for harvest, processing, and export is stabilizing, or perhaps more of their output (lower quality, lower price?) may be going to closer, burgeoning Asian markets. (We expect to have a more in-depth article on imported goat meat quality, quantity, and competition in a summer '06 issue of Goat Rancher).

Note that the **combined** total of federal slaughter and imported goat meat data indicates that there was less goat meat available for U.S. consumption in 2005 than in 2004. However, we believe these figures give an erroneous impression of the actual domestic goat meat available for consumption.

In point of fact, the numbers of goats slaughtered in **state**-inspected facilities are **not** routinely available for review by non-Agency persons; this is, we feel, a source of considerable error. For example, we were told by the TX Department of Health that in-state inspected goat slaughter numbered 59,886 in 2004 and 53,972 in 2005 (from 51 plants).

Also, the number of goats custom-slaughtered for fees in "locker plants" is unknown—yet another source of error. And, as mentioned in the Introduction, there are unknown, but apparently large, numbers of goats being sold (and "informally" slaughtered on-farm or off-premise, legally or illegally). Pickup, trailer, and even pot-loads of goats are frequently offered to buyers in FL NC, CA, TX, and elsewhere. Workers in orchards, packing plants, poultry processors, etc. are especially targeted by producers, "re-sellers", and truckers, alike.

These "uncounted" numbers of goats are, we feel, the explanation for the curious divergence of two lines shown in figure 2, namely, the U.S. meat goats inventory curve and the federal slaughter curve. Note that, beginning in 1993, the inventory curve rose much more sharply than the slaughter curve. Assuming the percentage off-take from the annual inventory numbers remained constant (or even increased a bit with improved management), kids and nannies were increasing sharply in real numbers, but they were **not** being federally- slaughtered at the **same** rate as before. Some of the "missing goats" were retained for breeding stock, but the others were being sold and slaughtered "informally". We make a wild-ass guess (that's, like, you know... an **estimate?**) that these non-federal/non-state inspected sales may constitute 10% or more of domestic goats (we imagine the IRS to be equally clueless).

In any case, if this estimate is more or less correct, this means that about 50 % of our consumption is federal/state-inspected domestic goat meat, while another 40% or so of our consumption is from (inspected) Australia/New Zealand facilities; the other 10% or so of our consumption remains, as it were, beneath the bureaucratic radar.

Goat meat demand

Most major indicators are the demand for goat meat will continue to increase, but readers should be aware that reliable estimates of demand are very difficult to determine. Conversations with industry players indicate that the current, aggregate supply of domestic and imported goat meat is sometimes inadequate to meet consumer needs.

Supply and demand curves can be very complicated to interpret because many factors influence prices of goat meat. Be that as it may, in past years traditional consumers have been willing to pay ever increasing prices for goat meat (as reflected by increased live-goat prices in those markets doing price reporting). However, the threshold (ceiling) price above which most consumers will resist paying more for goat meat, though real, is **not** predictable **before** it is reached.

However, there is no reason to expect that consumers of goat meat would not, at some point (price), begin to switch to other meats out of economic choice (similar consumer price responses/shifts among beef, chicken, and pork are well demonstrated). Contrarily, the demand for goat meat (and lamb) is heavily influenced by traditional, religion-based behavior which could militate against any precipitous shift

Producers should also be aware of yet another factor which might adversely affect future demand for goat meat. This is known as "generational shift" in demand, which occurs when younger people decide not to follow the eating patterns of their elders. Consumption of goat meat in the U.S. is concentrated among ethnic population groups whose children would seem particularly vulnerable to non-ethnic peer pressures. To illustrate, we were told, in 2000, by the biggest distributor of goat meat (and pork) in NYC-Chinatown that McDonald burgers and fast foods in general were already serious threats to traditional Chinese dishes among the second and third generation of immigrants.

Furthermore, a recent national market assessment of Latino buying habits substantiates that their rather rapid acculturation into "mainstream" eating habits (away from traditional fare) is sharply changing their selection of basic foodstuffs in the supermarkets. This finding must, we feel, be acknowledged and considered by those who are predicting "ever-increasing" demand for goat meat based, for the most part, on burgeoning numbers of current and newly-arriving Latinos. The influence of religious holidays in the Muslim culture will likely cause a slower rate of any generational changes in goat meat consumption.

Goat prices

Figure 3 documents the prices paid producers for the three grades of slaughter goats sold, and also the monthly throughput numbers, at the San Angelo, TX auction, 2002/05. The seasonality of supplies offered and price responses thereto are readily apparent; this pattern is repeated throughout TX and, with small variations, at public auctions in other states. But do note that the peak winter prices for '05 did not increase appreciably over those paid in '04. This is a break from the pattern of recent years. This may reflect many factors- drought-induced moderate sales mid-05, more truckload sales by ranchers directly to non-auction channels, or a possible approach of the "threshold/ceiling prices" discussed earlier.

We are told by industry players that this on-going seasonal supply pattern is **not adequately attuned** to processor/consumer needs; consequently, some consumers may not get sufficient quantities of the most desirable size or quality of goat meat when they want it. These supply/demand/ price relationships could possibly **warrant serious producer consideration for altering traditional kidding dates**—a target-marketing strategy to realize higher gross income (but, as always, cost-benefit calculations must be made as part of management decision-making).

Also, unusual trends are apparent in the current price pattern as compared to earlier findings. For example, the price differentials between the

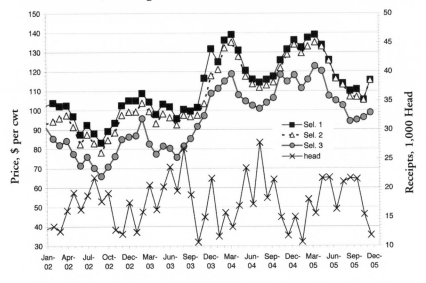

FIGURE 3

Average monthly price per hundredweight for 40 to 60 pound kids from Selection 1, 2, and 3 classifications and total monthly goat receipts, San Angelo, Texas Producers Auction.

top and second grades and between the second and third grades of kid goats were about 10 cents/lb in the mid-late nineties. Around 2000, the differential between the Selections 1 and 2 began to narrow to about 5 cents while the differential between Selection 2 and 3 increased to 11-12 cents/lb. During 2005 these differentials changed to just under 2 cents/lb between Selection 1 and 2 while Selection 3 prices were almost 14 cents below Selection 2.

These changing price responses suggest that the better goats are now heavier muscled with higher conformation scores while the poor quality goats are relatively less desirable to San Angelo buyers. Overall, the demand for, and buyer expectation of, higher quality goats seems to be increasing. Indeed, the Market Report for San Angelo now quotes prices in four, rather than three, grade categories: Selection 1, Selection 1 and 2 (low 1s and high 2s), Selection 2, and, only sporadically, for Section 3. As in the past, goats over 70 lb seem to sell somewhat cheaper/lb regardless of grade category (see weekly figures every Wednesday from www.ams. usda.gov/mnreports/sa_ls320.txt).

Furthermore, the *range* **of prices** *within* **grade** has increased appreciably in the 2000s. In 2002, the difference between high and low prices in both Selection 1 and 2 during the year was 20 cent/lb. In 2005, the difference between highest/lowest prices within Selection 1 across the months was 33 cents/lb; within Selection 2 the high/low difference was just under 30 cents/lb; for Selection 3 the figure was 28 cents/lb. We **speculate** that these wide price ranges within grade may reflect seasonal shortages in supply or possibly fluctuation occasioned by holiday demands of short duration.

From frequent discussions with owners, we are aware that fluctuations in price level received for goats of similar sizes and grades by producers in various geographical areas across time are thought to occur. However, the precise prices paid in certain regional markets and their relationship to each other and to the largest market, San Angelo, TX have not been reviewed and reported. (We are now collecting, collating, and analyzing such figures as are available; if all goes well, Goat Rancher will have the results to you by late summer).

Recent media articles have focused much interest in the meat goat industry, perhaps a function of increased publicity by various associations or local media using local interest stories. The potential for increased goat production in California and Alabama has been substantiated in reports by Sandra Solaiman. The California study can be accessed at sfc.ucdavis.edu/goat-meatpub.pdf and Dr. Solaiman may be contacted at ssolaim@tusk.edu.

Implications for Industry

The supply of goats does not meet aggregate consumer demand and has not done so for over a decade.

Imports of goat meat are necessary to supply deficit needs and to aid in maintaining consumer demand for this product. Contrary to what some say, we did not "lose" our market for goats to Australian competition—we voluntarily vacated it when we elected not to increase our meat goat supply fast enough as Angora goat numbers declined in the face of rising consumer demand.

Demand for carcasses of higher quality is increasing; this is reflected in the price differentials being paid for live Selections 1 and 2 as compared to Selection 3.

Seasonal variation in supplies of domestic goats does not accord close-ly with volumes/qualities of goat meat demand; imports do not always "fit" these deficit demands either.

Increasing the number kids weaned per doe exposed is more impor-tant, economically, for improving net enterprise returns than increasing sale weight which is, in turn, more important than improving conforma-tion selection grade.

Ken McMillin, Ph.D., is a meat scientist and professor, Dept. of Animal Sciences, LSU AgCenter, Baton Rouge, Louisiana, and Frank Pinkerton, Ph.D., The Goat Man, is a retired extension goat specialist, Martindale, Texas. They can be contacted at kmcmillin@agctr.lsu.edu or fpinkerton@austin.rr.com.

CHAPTER FORTY-ONE

The Need for Cooperation

S ome time after the end of his professional career, a retiree is occasionally seized with a near irresistible notion to offer, sought or not, some semblance of "end-of-tour" reporting to former colleagues, industry cohorts, and to (possibly) interested others. Such observations may be replete with professional commentary on accomplishments (real or imagined), problems encountered, current situation, (cautious) expectations, etc. Traditionally, the retiree feels entirely free to express cause-and-effect opinions, render value judgments, and forecast the probable while all too frequently grounded only in personal observations, private prejudices, and a serene confidence in his own sense of worth to the institution and/or industry he has served. Like Galbraith, I view modesty concerning noteworthy achievements as a greatly overrated virtue; contrarily, I am quick to say that, when I first left the University classroom for the real world in 1968, I experienced a precipitous decline in my powers of divination and the uncritical acceptance of my pronouncements; similarly, I suspect, with Galbraith.

(John Kenneth Galbraith, Canadian-born 1909, Distinguished Professor Emeritus, Harvard University, agricultural economist and noted author of economic and social history; valued advisor to political leaders, domestic and international. Among his myriad perceptive quotes in his observation that:

"Agriculture works well only under a widely accepted and much celebrated form of exploitation, that by the farmer of himself, his family and his immediate and loyal hired hands"—The Culture of Contentment, 1992.

Essentially, this keen observation is based on the long and documented record that farmers have historically subsidized consumer food and fiber expenditures while consistently earning returns to their labor, management, and capital far below those earned by corollary industrial and commercial sectors. With only rare exceptions across time and place, goat enterprises have demonstrated well this on-going economic phenomenon.)

Thus, though I will not preface my more positive sounding generalization with qualifier phrases such as: to the best of my knowledge. . .in my personal, unsubstantiated opinion, etc., readers are urged to be ever mindful of their absence; you are also urged to remember that, like the early French philosopher, M. Montaigne:

"All I say is by way of discourse….I should not speak so boldly if it were my due to be believed.

In any case, I illustrate my pleasure and my pride in having been associated with the development of our goat industry since 1979 by joining spiritually with one Samuel Deane, who, writing in the *New England Farmer,* 1790, said:

"Agriculture is one of the noblest employments to assist Nature in her bountiful productions. Instead of being ashamed of their employment, our laborious farmers should toss about their dung with an air of majesty". I now so toss…

The initiation and expansion of various aspects of our goat industry during the past century was due to personal initiative and private investment by owners seeking to increase returns/profits to their land and labor. In the time-honored rural tradition, such owners then freely shared their experiences with those neighbors similarly inclined toward novel opportunities. As may be imagined, this sharing mostly took the form of verbal communication with individuals or small local groups. This early, on-going generation and extension of practical results and economic applications concerning general agriculture is delightfully and effectively described by one Arthur Young who wrote in his *Rural Economy*, 1792:

"All gentlemen who make agriculture their business or amusement, should register their trials and either publish them themselves, or communicate them to others who will take that trouble. It is inconceivable how much the world would be benefited by such a conduct; matters relative to rural economics would receive a new face; every day would bring forth some valuable discovery, and every year that passed yield such an increase of knowledge, as to point and smooth the way to discoveries now unthought of. As far as a man's fortune will allow him to go, no amusement in the world equals the forming and conducting experiments in agriculture; to those, I mean, who have a taste for rural matters; nor can any business, however important, exceed, in real utility, this amusement. Experiments that are made with spirit and accuracy are of incomparable value in every branch of natural philosophy; those of agriculture, which is the most useful of these branches, must be particularly valuable".

This incredibly prescient paragraph recognizes the central role of agriculture in the lives of all people. In the U. S., as elsewhere, food and fiber production was then the basic occupation of the majority of the population; it was also the basic preoccupation of all citizens...starkly put, too few family foodstuffs, too few survivors. However, as populations increased in size and complexity over time, broad social and, ultimately, political pressures identified food and fiber production as a paramount societal concern, one that could not safely be left to localized, unorganized information exchanges of largely anecdotal information among farmers. As a result of this recognition of urgent national need, Congress in 1865 established a system of Cooperative Land Grant Colleges (one in each state) to generate research findings leading to improvements in farm output. (The word, Cooperative, refers to the required **joint**, but not necessarily **equal**, funding from Congress and State Legislatures); Congress initiated a second such program for Black Colleges in 1890).

Current Goat Research Needs, Contraints, and Opportunities

In early 2004, the Goat Rancher published an article in which I described, in broad profile, certain categories within the U.S. goat industry, as characterized by enterprise scale, scope, and goals, while in a fall article, 2004, I identified incipient difficulties likely to be encountered by novice goat owners. In 2002, the Goat Rancher presented my "take" on aspects of meat goat marketing. I cite these for your possible review, but also to document my long acquaintance with the industry, one which does have its problems—some of which seem "researchable", while others seem less amenable to investigation.

However, it must first be conceded that, as a group, we owners already have sufficient technical know-how, from whatever formal or informal sources, to manage the national herd of perhaps 2.5 million goats—sometimes profitably so. On the other hand, we do seem to have great difficulty in identifying *specific* production constraints, in *priortizing* among them, and, in particular, *making our collective needs known* to appropriate research entities/funding sources. Just poll a collection of goat owners informally for their views on goat industry research needs; the number and range of answers will be astounding. Indeed, I have devised a descriptive equation, possibly mathematically dubious, to quantify my findings: Pdv =Dsquared x SIn, (the volume of producer discussion is equal to the square of the number of discussants times the number of special interests represented). In the vernacular, we too seldom get our shit together.

Be that as it may, suppose a large number of us, acting (logically) through a State or Regional Association, *could/would* identify a researchable production constraint to industry growth/profitability....what to do? First, draft a written "position paper" describing the problem, its particulars and its extent, and, insofar as possible, quantifying its negative economic impact on a majority of producers. Secondly, take it to the Dean of Agriculture of your Land-Grant University or perhaps to his deputy (often called Director of the Experiment Station) or perhaps to the Chairman of the Animal Science Department. Alternatively, you could appear before the Administrator of the Extension Service or, a distinctly lesser personage, to your State Extension Livestock (goat) Specialist (I was such a fellow), who then could buck your request upwards through channels. In any case, the objective is to bring informed attention to your collective needs and, one may hope, get a full and frank discussion of possible responses.

And now for a dose of reality...the administrator you contact, invariably polite and sympathetic to petitioners and possibly even preliminarily persuaded by well-documented needs, will necessarily follow some form of Upper Administrative Policy Guidelines, i.e.,, he will have to convince the Final Decision-Maker and associated bean-counters of the economic relevance and possibly the political significance of the proposed research project. If so convinced, your project will go forward; if not, it becomes, with regrets, still-born.

More reality…there is a further, perhaps insidious factor at work in University precincts you should be aware of…most any research project nowadays is selected *in part* on what available funding sources will *authorize, in part* on its prospects for *scientific* publication, *in part* on the training, reputation and current *availability* of the needed investigator, and *in part* (one may hope) on its practical relevance to its target clientele (that's you). But, once approved, done, and published, extension specialists have the opportunity/onus to deliver the findings to you.

Even more reality…most federal agricultural research dollars are distributed to States as lump sums (not partitioned by crop, livestock, etc.). They are targeted, according to USDA *fiat*, for "basic science", i.e., to *fundamental investigations.* Consequently, very few of these funds are currently allocated for applied/practical research projects (the kind of help most goat producers most often need). Note, too, that the USDA has its' own extensive research capability, the Agriculture Research Service, with many subject matter areas of interest and at several locations (some have State "partners", some not). Note, too, that Congress itself may direct, and specifically fund, USDA to undertake politically-sensitive research (and extension) activities aimed at solving high visibility, national or regional problems (e.g., animal/plant disease control, food safety issues, etc.).

Goat organizations should know that USDA also has, from time to time, certain "ear-marked funds" available for livestock producer groups seeking direct federal help. The competition for these grants is fierce, and technical competence can sometimes be usefully abetted by political influence. Readers should recognize that goat owners constitute a minority group with few and less vocal supporters (prospective voters); as such, they are critically under-represented at decision-making levels—sad, but true. But, when a grant *is* forthcoming, producer groups commonly "sub" the execution of the research project to University or other qualified personnel. (Such funds powered my early investigations (with South Carolina, North Carolina, and New York personnel) concerning goat marketing and my recent work with Louisiana co-workers concerning development of goat grading standards).

Currently, there are substantial goat research efforts at Langston U (OK), Texas A&MU-San Angelo, Fort Valley S U(GA), and Virginia S U; smaller efforts, due perhaps to less funding and/or Administrative interest, are found in NC, FL, TN, and LA. Additionally, Veterinary investigations have been conducted, primarily in TX, NY, MD, CA, WA and OR. Substantial goat research is also conducted in France, Israel, South Africa, India, Malaysia, Australia, and, more recently, in China; some has/will have relevance to our own needs.

In addition to federal and state monies given to Universities as described above, some State Departments of Agriculture occasionally distribute modest sums for livestock and goat activities (but rarely for research projects *per se)*. The few goat funds made available to date have gone mostly to marketing studies and to industry development programs in TX, OK, LA, NC, KY, VA, and NY.

Goat groups occasionally inquire as to how they might get a commercial company to research/develop a product to meet a particular industry need (parasite control is the paramount concern identified). Unfortunately, pharmaceutical companies feel they can not afford even the financial outlay necessary to obtain FDA "goat labeling" for existing health products, much less justify the expense of new product development, testing, and approval. Thus, prospects for novel, effective products are not good, not only because of expense, but also because goat owners simply do not constitute a sufficient *size* of market to warrant such products; again, sad but true. Commercial companies *do* formulate goat feeds and mineral/vitamin supplements by using existing data from various sources, but they rarely do goat nutrition research *per se*. Incidentally, I have never known any feed company to utilize any sort of public (on-farm) comparative demonstration of their products. The logistics of such an undertaking are admittedly complex and daunting; besides, their product might not win.

Current Goat Extension Needs, Contraints, and Opportunities

The need for agricultural extension activities was recognized early on by one Jared Elliot, who wrote in 1760 in *Essays upon Field-Husbandry In New England:*

"Useful Arts are sometimes lost for want of being put into Writing. Tradition is a very slippery Tenure, and a slender Pin to bear any great weight for a long time.....whoever has made any Observation or Discoveries, altho' it be but a Hint, and looks like a small Matter, yet if pursued and improved, may be of publick Service....I am sure I should have been glad of such an History of Facts (as imperfect as it is). It would have afforded me Light, Courage, and Instruction".

The need for retaining and extending agricultural technology was again recognized in 1826 by one Leonard Lathrop in *The Farmer's Library*, who warned us that:

"For want of records, much useful knowledge is continually lost. Though many individuals have derived advantages to themselves from experiments, but few have recorded them. Even those who make experiments are liable to forget them, so as to give incorrect representation of them when they attempt to relate them".

And so it came to pass, in the sometimes leisurely manner of political and bureaucratic affairs everywhere, that the USDA in 1902 created the joint Federal/State Cooperative Agricultural Extension Service. Its charge, initially, was to disseminate research results to crop and livestock producers, primarily through the Land Grant University System. (In later years, the AES added programs in home economics, human nutrition, child care, etc.). Goat owners are locally impacted by the Extension Service via its' County Extension Agents, who are necessarily "generalists" in that they field questions, supply information, and conduct training for a wide variety of subject matter areas including 4-H youth programs—for which goats have been particularly well suited.

At the next level are State Extension Specialists, those with in-depth training/expertise in a certain subject matter area, e.g., animal science, crop science, economics, sociology, etc., and, within such areas, specialization in, say, livestock nutrition, physiology, or genetics. Some specialists may have particular expertise concerning beef cattle, poultry, sheep/goats, etc. and may be stationed at the LGU campus or at regional research/extension Centers in the State. They serve primarily as technical backstop to County Agents, but also interact directly with farmers and ranchers and sometimes conduct result-demonstrations on-site with cooperating farmers. Some also do occasional joint activities with other

USDA entities such as Forest Service, Bureau of Land Management, and Natural Resources Conservation Service. (I was just such a Specialist for 14 years in TX/OK and, on request, in other states with interests in developing a goat sector).

Historically, only those states with large populations of goats (TX) and sheep (Rocky Mt States. OH, VA) had State Specialists for these species. However, in the recent past, goat populations have increased dramatically in the southeastern states; consequently, a number of full- and part-time State Extension Specialists are now available to goat owners there; so also in NY, MD, and VT. Note that goat numbers first expanded; only thereafter were extension efforts instituted in response to owner needs. Oklahoma was the exception in that it established, in 1983, a goat extension (and research) program, at Langston University, with the express purpose of developing a goat industry where one did not exist.

Goat extension efforts take many forms, among them Newsletters, Field-Days, on- or off-campus seminars/training sessions or demonstrations. Early on, there were bulletins, fact sheets, and leaflets, but, with increasing printing/distribution costs and, particularly, with the advent of Internet service, these have all but disappeared. Once an Extension staple activity, on-site visitations to owners for problem identification/solving have now declined markedly due to cost considerations, however, telephone/email exchanges still enable some personalized interactions.

One of the ways Extension Specialists *could* offer counsel to goat owners, widely and economically, is via publication in monthly magazines having substantial regional/national circulation. Curiously enough, this opportunity seems under-used to date, for whatever reasons…perhaps the available research findings have not been yet published in research journals (a bureaucratic no-no)…perhaps the research findings, though of scientific and, possibly, of long-term merit, are of too little obvious/practical value to current producers…perhaps the Extension Agent is too swamped with corollary duties…perhaps he/she feels inadequate as a writer of "lay-language" articles…perhaps he/she perceives that their Administrator values publication in more scientific venues as somehow professionally preferable to producer education via popular periodicals (which are certainly more often read by goat owners than are the more "learned" publications.

The "quality" of goat extension efforts is said by informed and thoughtful goat owners to vary widely, possibly due to Administrative interest/funding levels or to differences in personnel qualifications/interest, and possibly, I have seen, to erroneous levels of expectation and lack of positive response from the producers themselves. In any case, Extension Agents are not the only source of technical information available to goat owners. In addition to industry magazines, goat producers have available books on herd health, basic nutrition, and herd management as well as useful information from suppliers of needed goods. Too, Breed publications commonly contain some useful information among their more voluminous promotional materiel, Show results, and occasional puff pieces.

Self-Help for Goat Owners

Perhaps one of the better, immediately available sources for goat production/marketing information is person-to-person conversation. Indeed, this strategy was so noted in 1800 by one Thomas Fessenden in *The Register of Arms*, who said:

"What may seem to some persons as merely commonplace information may, perhaps, prove valuable to others, whose time may have been devoted to pursuits of a different nature:

This advice to seek private counsel (e.g., from one goat owner by another goat owner) can be—and often is a cheap and effective way to learn. Contrarily, such one-on-one discussion can be, as many unhappily know from experience, a classic case of the blind- leading-the-blind; in short, know your source, or be prepared to be occasionally led astray. The difficulty for greenhorns is that, being poorly informed, they can't readily distinguish among the "facts" being offered, all with the best of intentions, of course.

A geographically close collection of goat owners will, almost invariably, hit on the notion to form some sort of collective group for the furtherance of shared goals and objectives, however defined as to organizational structure and program of work needed to accomplish their aims. Sometimes, particularly early on in its' life, a newly formed group will proceed enthusiastically, harmoniously, and effectively. In other instances, with the passage of time, there is a tendency—indeed, a near certainty—for contrary personalities to emerge, clash, and precipitate crises —to the detriment and, occasionally, to the dissolution of the group. Such unfortunate occurrences are clearly adverse to group harmony, to effective communication, and, worse of all, to sustained organizational effectiveness. However, those group members with a bent toward cooperation, compromise, and consideration of others (too frequently in the too-silent majority) can—indeed, must seize the stage, as it were, and regain the upper hand in order for the group to proceed effectively. If so, they can readily and appropriately identify with an earlier advocate of communalism-of-purpose, one James Donaldson who in 1700 wrote in *The Undoubted Art of Thriving*:

"That every Man should imploy himself not only for the advancing of his own Interest, but likewise that he may propagate the Welfare of others, will, I suppose, be sooner granted than practiced...it is necessary, that some be imployed one way, and some another, so that each may attain to some Competent Degree of Knowledge of, and Dexterity in the Vocation or Imployment he Professes, so that every one may be Useful and Assisting to another, and by mutual Good Correspondence with one another, all may live Comfortable together".

Localized or multi-county goat organizations that arrange technical assistance sessions, conduct Shows and assorted Sales, do Youth activities, etc. to successful and encouraging effect, may then decide to look further afield. They may perceive the need for, and possibilities of, creating (or joining other groups to form) a State Association, or even a Regional or National Association of like-minded (concerned/intelligent/forward-thinking) goat owners. Their primary goal would likely be *actionable interests* in industry betterment, however defined, or perhaps in pursuing State or National Government grants, or Federal legislation to fend off potentially intrusive regulations, or to obtain favorable regulatory assistance in marketing, or possibly for legal intervention to protect themselves from international competition.

These interests (wishes) are, by definition, noble, possibly achievable, but...they are also invariably difficult, costly, and potentially enervating for members. Particularly so for those individuals (usually elected leaders) within the enlarged organization who physically carry the onus, i.e., who *do* the organizational fine-tuning of the Association and thereafter *guide* its operational logistics, and (only then) *obtain consensus* on the proposed course of action, and finally, *make* the time-consuming and expensive trips to Washington for jaw-to-jaw meetings with Congressional mover-

and-shakers…well, for *them*, the glory, always fleeting, may not adequately compensate. They may need, and certainly deserve, sustained financial and emotional support. I do concede that Association members are permitted, even obligated to provide (constructive) criticism, but they should also be sparing in their (sometimes) uninformed criticism of the chosen leaders—at least until they themselves have walked-the-walk (Thereafter, such critics would likely be a noticeably subdued and certainly more understanding—of issues and personal sacrifice).

A concluding word on goat Cooperatives, whether for buying goods or for selling animals or products, or for seeking political influence for various purposes. In over 50 years in the livestock industry, I have encountered few such successful enterprises, no matter how valid their chosen cause. Failures, early and late, have been the norm, for whatever particular reasons. A *major* reason for failure, I have come to believe, is that, to be successful and sustainable, Cooperative members would have to practice a nearly untenable togetherness over time. Such close personal interaction may well require more virtue than mere mortals can stomach. Sometime, after a Bud-Lite or two, I phrase it as: like Socialism, a Cooperative is way too Christian a notion to ever catch on widely.

I close these free-ranging, incomplete observations with yet another delightful quote, all the while conceding that *I* have in no way "fully satisfied your desire to know"—but even a modest effort can be a useful one, so…

"Thus gentle Reader I have (I trust) fully satisfied thy desire In as many things as are needful to be knowne: wherefore I commit my little Booke to thy gentle judgement. If thou maist receive any profit or commodities thereby, I shalbe glad to it; and if not, favorably let it pass from thee to others, whose knowledge and experience is lesse than thine therein, that they may gather such things as to them are strange, though to thee well knowne before."— *Thomas Hill,* The Arts of Gardening, 1608.

PART EIGHT

Cocinar
Chevito

Recipes for Cooking Goat Meat

Cevon Chili Verde

INGREDIENTS:
4 pounds goat meat
2 onions, finely chopped
1 glove garlic, minced
2 small cans chopped green chilies
2 can diced tomatoes (with green chilies is fine too)
1 tsp. Cumino

Cook on low heat in crock-pot until meat is falling apart.
Check occasionally – add water if necessary.

Serve with flour tortillas, shredded lettuce, sour cream
and pico de gallo.

Caston Creek's Pico de Gallo

Mix together 3-4 chopped Roma tomatoes, one small diced
cucumber, ¼ cup minced onion, 1-2 finely chopped jalapeño
peppers (remove seeds first), 1 bunch cilantro, chopped, 1 tsp.
white vinegar. If you like things really hot, add more peppers and
leave in the seeds.

Caston Creek Salsa

INGREDIENTS:
1 can diced tomatoes
1 can tomatoes and green chilies
1 bunch of cilantro, wash and remove stems
garlic salt
fresh ground pepper
1 small onion, optional

Combine ingredients in a blender and process to desired consistency.

Serve with tortilla chips as an accompaniment or an appetizer with Mexican food.

Enchiladas Verde with Sour Cream

INGREDIENTS:
3 cups cooked shredded boiled or grilled cabrito
1 can (4 oz) chopped green chilies
½ tsp salt
1 can green chili enchilada sauce
½ cup milk
1 small container sour cream
12 corn tortillas
2 cups shredded Monterey jack cheese

Mix together shredded cabrito, green chilies and salt. Combine sauce, milk and sour cream. Fry tortillas in hot oil for a few seconds on each side until limp. Dip each tortilla in the sauce mixture; fill with ¼ cup cabrito mix; roll up and place seam side down in 13 x 9" baking dish. Pour remaining sauce over casserole. Sprinkle with cheese. Bake at 425°F for 15 minutes, until bubbly.

Chevito Champignon

INGREDIENTS:
1-2 lbs of chevon medallions
1 lb fresh mushrooms, sliced
2 Tbsp. Cooking sherry
Mrs. Dash Herb and Garlic
½ stick butter or 2 Tbsp. Olive Oil

Sauté sliced mushrooms in butter or oil until lightly browned; move to one side of the skillet and add the medallions of chevon. Brown medallions on one side, turn browned side up and season with Mrs. Dash Herb and Garlic; add cooking sherry and cover simmering on low heat 20 to 30 minutes until done. Serve with rice pilaf and fresh steamed asparagus.

Garlic Sour Cream Chevon

INGREDIENTS:
3 lbs Chevon Medallions
1 stick butter
1 cup seasoned bread crumbs

MIX TOGETHER:
1 small container of sour cream
2 tsp white wine Worcestershire sauce
2 cloves of fresh garlic, minced
dash of white pepper to taste
1 T. lemon juice

Coat medallions with sour cream mixture and place in a greased casserole dish. Spoon any remaining mixture into the baking dish. Cut butter into breadcrumbs and sprinkle evenly over the chevon. Bake uncovered for 1 hour at 350°F in preheated oven.

Pinchitos Morunos

INGREDIENTS:
1 lb. of goat meat cut into cubes
2 garlic cloves, finely chopped
1 tsp. curry powder
1 tsp. salt
½ tsp. coriander seeds
1 tsp. paprika
¼ tsp dried thyme
freshly ground black pepper
¼ cup olive oil
1 tsp. lemon juice

Crush the garlic with the salt & combine the remaining spices, oil & lemon juice. Marinate the cabrito cubes in a shallow dish for several hours. Skewer and barbecue over or broil under a high heat for about 3 minutes per side.

Shoulder Roast in White Wine

INGREDIENTS:
4 lb. Chevon shoulder roast
Fresh garlic
1 bottle of sauterne wine

With a sharp knife, make slits in the shoulder roast. Insert slivers of fresh garlic into the slits. Marinade the roast overnight in the white wine, turning occasionally to get marinade on all sides.

Bake covered, in 325°F oven for 2 hours or until done. Serve with oven roasted potatoes and steamed broccoli.

Oven roasted potatoes: Peel and cube potatoes, toss in melted butter, place on a baking sheet and sprinkle with salt, fresh ground pepper, and rosemary. Cook during last hour of roasting chevon.

Chevon & Artichoke Casserole

INGREDIENTS:
3 lbs. Thinly sliced chevon
salt and pepper to taste
½ cup flour
½ stick butter
½ lbs. fresh mushrooms
3 Tbsp. flour
2 Tbsp. butter
1 can chicken broth
3 T. cooking sherry
1 can artichoke hearts

Season chevon with salt and pepper, dip in flour, brown in 2 Tbsp. butter (or olive oil) in heavy skillet, remove meat and place in the bottom of a large baking dish.

Melt another 2 Tbsp butter in skillet and add sliced fresh mushrooms, cook until limp, sprinkle with 2-3 Tbsp. flour, stir for a few minutes to cook the flour. Slowly add 1 can of chicken broth and 3 Tbps. of cooking sherry, simmer stirring until sauce thickens. Remove sauce from heat. Add artichoke hearts to baking dish and pour mushroom sauce over chevon and artichokes. Cover and bake 40 minutes at 375°F.

Chevon Paprika

INGREDIENTS:
2 Tbsp. olive oil and 2 Tbsp. butter mixed
3-4 lbs stew sized chunks of goat meat
1 small onion, chopped
1 clove garlic, minced
1 can crushed tomatoes
2 Tbsp. Hungarian Paprika
1 tsp. basil
½ tsp. oregano
3 Tbps. flour
½ cup whipping cream
½ cup sour cream
1 Tbsp. cooking sherry
1 can chicken stock

Saute onion in heavy skillet (or deep kettle) in butter and oil until transparent, add minced garlic, continue to stir, cooking for one minute more. Add tomatoes, paprika, basil, oregano, and chicken stock. Stir well and add chevon. Cover and cook 40 minutes, simmering slowly. Remove chevon with a slotted spoon to a covered baking dish to keep warm. Combine flour and cream, mixing well until smooth. Slowly stir flour and cream mixture into stock simmering in skillet. Stir until sauce thickens. Add sour cream and sherry stirring well. Serve over chevon on a bed of hot buttered egg noodles.

Chevito Meatloaf

INGREDIENTS:
2 lbs of ground goat meat
1 lb ground lean pork (optional but a nice mix)
1 finely chopped onion
¼ tsp. garlic powder
¼ tsp. black pepper
1 Tbsp. spicy spaghetti seasoning
1 egg, well beaten
¼ cup catsup mixed with 1 small can tomato sauce
1 tsp. honey mustard

Mix all ingredients, saving back half of the tomato sauce/catsup mixture to pour over top of loaf before baking. Bake in greased loaf pan 1 hour at 350°F.

Note: Leftover meatloaf can be sliced and served cold as a delicious alternative to lunchmeat.

Chicken Fried Chevito

INGREDIENTS:
2 lbs. Thinly sliced round of chevon
fresh ground black pepper
garlic salt
1 cup flour
2 eggs beaten with ¼ cup of milk

Tenderize round steaks, season with pepper and garlic salt. Double dip: first dip steaks in flour, then egg mixture, then back to the flour mixture. Set aside on platter or work surface to rest while heating grease in heavy skillet. Fry until golden brown. Drain on paper towels or brown grocery bag paper. Serve with cream gravy.

Caston Creek Cream Gravy
Save 3 to 4 Tbsp. grease (pan drippings) from skillet that fried chevito, drain off remaining grease. Add 3-4 Tbsp. flour to pan drippings, stir over medium heat for a couple of minutes to cook flour. Slowly add approximately 3 cups of milk to grease and flour mixture, stirring constantly. Mixture will thicken to gravy consistency. Remove from heat and serve.

Polish Style Chevito

INGREDIENTS:
1 lb. Smoked goat sausage, sliced into bite size rounds
1 large yellow onion, sliced
1 small head of green cabbage, sliced
salt and pepper to taste
1 box of bow tie pasta, cooked al dente and drained
½ stick of butter

Saute onion in butter until transparent, add sliced sausage stirring until heated. Add cabbage, continue cooking over medium heat for 3 to 4 minutes, stirring frequently until cabbage is limp. Salt and Pepper to taste. Add cooked pasta, toss and serve. A cold fruit or jello salad makes a nice side for this dish.

Crock Pot Chevon

INGREDIENTS:
3 lbs. Chevon roast
Dry onion soup mix
1 can of diced tomatoes
1 lb. Fresh mushrooms, sliced
1 onion quartered
1 bag of baby carrots
2 medium sized potatoes cubed

Put roast in crock pot with 1 can of diced tomatoes, sprinkle with onion soup mix. Put on in the morning and cook all day on low. Add water as needed. 1 hour before serving, add remaining vegetables. This is a good recipe for those days when you plan to spend most of it outside rather than in the kitchen. Serve with hot rolls, a garden salad and ice tea and no one will go away complaining!

Nana's Envy of Tuscany

POT 1: Marinara

SAUTÉ: 2 small cans of mushroom pieces (or use approximate equivalent of fresh if available) in olive oil with 1 or more links of goat sausage thinly sliced.

ADD:
¼ cup finely chopped celery
1 cup finely chopped onion
1 Tbsp. dried basil (or fresh equivalent if available)
1 can diced tomatoes
1 jar generic marinara sauce

SIMMER: to combine flavors for 30 minutes or longer as desired

POT 2: Pasta (start preparation about 15 minutes prior to eating)

ADD:
6 cups wide egg noodle pasta to 4 quarts boiling water —
cook per directions (about 9 minutes)
DRAIN: pasta, set aside, return pot to stove and

MELT: ½ stick butter

ADD:
1 cup heavy cream
1 cup shredded parmesan

STIR: over low heat until well blended

Nana's Envy of Tuscany
(continued)

Return pasta to cream sauce in pot and toss

SERVE: tossed pasta topped with marinara sauce

Add a nice Chianti, a hot baguette (salad if you wish) and Enjoy!

Italian Chevon Olive Garden Potato Soup

INGREDIENTS:
1 small sweet onion, chopped
4-6 medium – large golden potatoes, cleaned and chopped
(peeling optional)
1 quart chicken broth
1 cup fresh chopped kale (remove tough center stem)
Italian styled goat sausage, sliced into disks
Salt to taste (remember chicken broth is salty and the sausage
will add seasoning to the mix too so don't overdo the salt)

Sauté sausage in olive oil, add chopped onion; simmer until
onion is transparent.

Add chicken broth and potatoes, simmer until potatoes
are tender.

Add 1 cup heavy cream, stir.

Sprinkle with fresh ground black pepper and parmesan cheese,
garnish with kale, and serve.

This is a good knock off of a popular Italian restaurant mainstay.

The Caston Creek Ranch
Secret Goat Ration Recipe

*16+% Goat Ration****

# Lbs	Ingredient	%CP	% Protein in Ration
500	Oats	12	3
400	Alfalfa Pellets	17	3.4
350	Soy Bean Meal	46*	8.05
500	Whole Corn	8	2
149	Cotton Seed Hulls	3.8	0.2831
5	Cane Molasses	5.8	0.0145
50	Ground Limestone	16.7476%	CP
25	18.5% Dical Phosphate		
10	Moorman High Copper Mineral (check with your vet)		
10	Ammonium Chloride		
1	Bovatech – use only with your vet's approval (at approx 200 mg/# fed) 2000#		

*   CP can run a little higher

** If you have a mill run this for you, you may have to call it calf creep feed – at the time we developed this feed, Bovatech was not approved for goats (nothing is!)

Caston Creek Ranch
Secret Goat Ration Recipe
(continued)

** It's true we don't believe in supplementing *unless* there is no
choice i.e. your forage is lousy, you have no browse, had a
drought and didn't plant winter pasture or some combination
thereof. *Quality foragae* first always! *But* if you need to supplement – late trimester does, lactating mothers, weaned kids
or young breeding bucks – this recipe worked for us.

*Note: Use at your own risk. We guarantee neither the results nor the
safety of the foregoing mixture when used to supplement your animals.
We offer this simply in the spirit of sharing our experience with you.*

PART NINE

Snapshots
in Time

1986-1999

To church on Sunday mornings

(above) Mandy's Christmas puppy "Bear" and (left) Mike and Mandy comfort "Lucky" the orphan calf

Multi-species babies!

*Guardian dog
in training*

*The Tomlinson Boys:
Papa with Greg,
Scott, David and
Yella*

Photos © Gene Blackwell

Photos © Gene Blackwell

Photos © Gene Blackwell

Photos © Gene Blackwell